# THE BODYT ▮▮▮

G000114486

# Vital

## Food Facts

## &

## 90 DAY DIET DIARY

## JUDY COLE

Published by Alchemist Publishing International.

Alchemist Publishing, UK
1-18 Hams Crescent
Knightbridge
London
SW1X OLL

www.judycole.co.uk
www.thebodytalks.com

First published 2003
First reprint 2004

Copyright: Judy Cole
Design Copyright: Judy Cole

British Library Cateloguing in Publication Data
ISBN 0-9546950-1-1

All rights reserved. No part of this publication may be reproduced in any material form
(including photography or storing in any medium by electronic means) without the written
permission of the copyright holders. Applications for the copyright holders written permission
to reproduce any part of this publication should be addressed to the publishers.
Any person acting in contravention of this copyright will be liable to criminal prosecution
and the civil claims for damages.

Designed by Jonathan Court & Judy Cole

Alchemist
PUBLISHING

# ABOUT THE AUTHOR

No manual is complete without an in-depth questions and answers section. A manual as complex as nutrition, with its myriad of topics and complexities so vital to our everyday health, will inevitably pull up numerous questions for those of us on the quest for the truth about how food and diet really affects our health. In this book you will find the answers to the questions I had when I began working in the field of nutrition and was faced with endless conflicting and confusing opinions about different foods. Should we eat eggs, and how many, and why were they so bad for us if man had eaten eggs for thousands of years? Why is meat so bad for us for the same reason and why do I get fat on fruit when it is supposed to be so good for us?

In the Body Talks Programme, which this diary compliments, the questions of how to eat for life and truly heal your weight are already addressed. The simple, natural but sometimes startling programme is the result of eight years of using a special gift I have of 'talking' directly to your body's subconscious and 'asking', with the help of muscle testing, what food you really want and how foods affect us. Directly from the horses' mouth so to speak. Over the last four years, I have tested and helped over 2000 clients from all over the world at my clinic in Dubai, in the United Arab Emirates. Some of the recommendations from their bodies, flew right in the face of standard guidelines and nutritional training. But the results spoke for themselves and hundreds of people felt the benefits of following their body's advice. Further in-depth research into the studies behind these public guidelines, highlighted, in my mind, important findings that had been conveniently ignored in the interest of economics or because they didn't confirm what the scientist had set out to prove. The body has been my greatest teacher, it doesn't lie. We are all connected to a universal all knowing consciousness that has our best interests at heart. We just needed a way of accessing it.

Ultimately, the biggest shortfall of all nutritional studies of the past hundred years has been to omit recording the blood types of each person taking part in the study. Our blood type is a major influencing factor in how people react and digest the same food. A predominance of A blood types, unwittingly comprising a study looking at how our bodies react to meat or milk, will result in a very different outcome than a study comprising predominantly O blood types. As very few, if any, studies to date have taken this vital factor into account, the studies are to my mind, null and void. We are not the same, not only divided by the four blood types with the subgroups of positive and negative, but are also products of our cultural inheritance and the foods our ancestors ate for thousands of years

I also have a vested interest in this topic, actually a life or death interest in it! In 1995, I suffered my first attack of Multiple Sclerosis and was unable to walk without great difficulty for four months. I was at that time working as a remedial massage and injury therapist with professional sports teams and individuals, such as Leeds United AFC, the Olympic ice skaters, Jane Torvill and Christopher Dean, and the Northern Ballet Company. I have studied natural medicine extensively and have an MSc in Sport Science.

The cause of my symptoms, and I have since found out the cause of many other sufferers of Multiple Sclerosis, was entirely food intolerances. Several everyday foods, which we all eat and I had innocently eaten all my life, were not tolerated by my blood type and genetic imprint. Each time I ate them, my B blood type reacted to a protein in the food, identifying it as an invader and not a friend. In my case, the rogue proteins interfered with the brain chemistry and short circuited the chemical messages from my brain to the nerves. By chance I eliminated all the foods which caused the condition in the early days, but which I now know, having 'asked' my body, were mainly chicken, wheat, yeast, tea and coffee.

So I am truly an independent explorer into the truth about food, how it's made, what it contains and how foods and different combinations of them affect us. I have been on a strict diet for eight years now, and having suffered a constant weight battle since childhood, am now in great mental and physical shape. The depth and effectiveness of The Body Talks Programme in healing weight has proved itself on hundreds of clients, who in the process have found long term health conditions and illnesses have often disappeared.

The Vital food facts in this book have evolved from my extensive, independent and unbiased research under the guidance of our greatest guide and teacher, our own bodies. I am confident that these guidelines will serve you well, but I am very open to any further information or to anyone wishing to challenge my findings with new insights. After all, this is for the benefit of all of us.

The Vital food facts is combined with a 90 day diary, will be a great help to record your progress as you heal your body and your weight over the next few months. Keeping a diary will enable you to watch the patterns I have described in the detox and the weight loss graphs in 'The Body Talks Programme'. It will enhance your understanding of how your individual body reacts to different foods. In the future you can always refer back to it, to remind yourself of what works for you.

I wish you all the best and hope you enjoy discovering your health and inherent natural beauty as much as I have.

Judy Cole

## WEIGH AND MEASURE DAY

weight ................... kgs/lbs
waist ........................... cm
hips ........................... cm
bust/chest .................... cm
top of thigh.................. cm
top of arm .................... cm
knee........................... cm
calf ........................... cm

INITIAL OBSERVATIONS AND NOTES ABOUT YOUR HEALTH BEFORE STARTING THIS PROGRAMME

.....................................
.....................................
.....................................
.....................................
.....................................
.....................................
.....................................
.....................................
.....................................
.....................................

# DAY 1

**TODAYS DATE**................................................................................................................................

**Quality of sleep:**................................**Number of hours slept**:............................................
Scale: 1 = poor  Scale: 10 = deep and refreshing

**Vitality factor in morning** (scale 1= very tired, hungover, not well, dying)
(scale: 10 = full of energy, clear headed, refreshed, generally fantastic) ...................................................out of 10

**Breakfast**

Time eaten: ..........................................
Food:...............................................................................................................................................
.........................................................................................................................................................

**Snack**

Time eaten: ..........................................
Food:...............................................................................................................................................
.........................................................................................................................................................

**Lunch**

Time eaten: ..........................................
Food:...............................................................................................................................................
.........................................................................................................................................................
.........................................................................................................................................................

**Snack**

Time eaten: ..........................................
Food:...............................................................................................................................................
.........................................................................................................................................................

**Dinner**

Time eaten: ..........................................
Food:...............................................................................................................................................
.........................................................................................................................................................
.........................................................................................................................................................

**Exercise**:.......................................................................................................................................
.........................................................................................................................................................
**Quality of day out of 10**...............................................................................................................

# HOW TO USE THIS DIARY

In this book you will find interesting and useful information about food and nutrition that should answer many questions you may have from reading 'The Body Talks Programme'. Interspersed with these entries is a 90 day diary for you to record your progress as you go.

On day one, weigh yourself and take your measurements as indicated on the next page. You are only going to do this at the beginning of each new week, i.e. every eighth day. This column is recorded on the top of the left hand page for you. If you wish you can do this fortnightly, but it is important that you do NOT get on the scales between these times. Do not become obsessed with your weight. Your weight will often not tell the whole story of what is happening inside your body. As you lose fat on 'The Body Talks Programme', you will also put on muscle and the scales stay the same even though your body is transforming itself inside. Muscle is two and a half times heavier than fat. Just follow the programme and let your body do its job without you getting on its case! Remember, it is no good wanting to weigh under nine stone ladies if you have no muscle mass. You can still be underweight and flabby. Scales are both misleading and psychological killers. Judge your weight loss by your clothes, your well being, your vitality factor and by what other people say. You are aiming to reach a weight and size that makes you feel happy; at which good honest friends tell you that you look good at. You may never have the type of body that will look like Cindy Crawford or David Beckham and life is too short to spend your precious days battling for the unattainable. Settle for adopting a new healthy way of eating that will guide you for life, even if you carry more than your ideal social body norms would have you be.

As you follow this programme during the first three months, you will notice the pattern of detox that is described in the programme. It is a fascinating journey and by recording it in this diary, you will see the pattern emerge and have a record to refer back to in the future about what works best for you.

Everyday, record exactly what you ate at each meal. Try and be fairly accurate about quantities. For example, half an apple, two ryvita, one third

## NOTES AND OBSERVATIONS

..................................
..................................
..................................
..................................
..................................
..................................
..................................
..................................
..................................
..................................
..................................
..................................
..................................
..................................
..................................
..................................
..................................
..................................
..................................
..................................
..................................
..................................
..................................
..................................
..................................
..................................
..................................
..................................
..................................

# DAY 2

**TODAYS DATE** ...................................................................................................................................................................

**Quality of sleep:** ...............................**Number of hours slept**: ...................................................................................
Scale: 1 = poor   Scale: 10 = deep and refreshing

**Vitality factor in morning** (scale 1= very tired, hungover, not well, dying)
(scale: 10 = full of energy, clear headed, refreshed, generally fantastic) ...........................................................out of 10

**Breakfast**

Time eaten: ..........................................

Food:....................................................................................................................................................................

...............................................................................................................................................................................

**Snack**

Time eaten: ..........................................

Food:....................................................................................................................................................................

...............................................................................................................................................................................

**Lunch**

Time eaten: ..........................................

Food:....................................................................................................................................................................

...............................................................................................................................................................................

...............................................................................................................................................................................

**Snack**

Time eaten: ..........................................

Food:....................................................................................................................................................................

...............................................................................................................................................................................

**Dinner**

Time eaten: ..........................................

Food:....................................................................................................................................................................

...............................................................................................................................................................................

...............................................................................................................................................................................

**Exercise**: ............................................................................................................................................................

...............................................................................................................................................................................

**Quality of day out of 10** ....................................................................................................................................

cup cottage cheese, large salad etc.

Each morning judge the quality of sleep that night and the hours slept. '10' would be a deep refreshing sleep without interruptions and disturbing dreams. '1' would be the very worst night of tossing and turning, bad dreams, aches and pains and so on. Then give yourself a score for your vitality factor for how you feel at breakfast. A '10' would be full of energy, clear headed, refreshed and generally feeling healthy and ready for the day. A '1' would be a deep detox of drugged feeling, headache, generally exhausted, dying!

If you exercise that day, record what exercise you did and make a note of what time of day you exercised. This may effect the way you feel and it is important to notice a pattern. In this way you should discover what is your best time of day to exercise, to suit your immune system.

Then give yourself a general mark for quality of day out of '10'. Judge it on well being, energy levels, adherence to the programme, number of times you cheated, (or hopefully didn't!).

Finally in the left hand column there is space to record symptoms of your detox, any observations you make about your progress, or any little note to yourself that may be helpful in the future, such as a good restaurant you found, or a new recipe.

On every eighth day review your week and give yourself an overall mark for each entry. These will all then be recorded on the graphs on page 164 and 166 so you can clearly see the pattern and relationship between these factors over the 90 day period.

## NOTES AND OBSERVATIONS

# DAY 3

**TODAYS DATE** ................................................................................................................................................................

**Quality of sleep:** ..............................**Number of hours slept**: ..........................................................................
Scale: 1 = poor  Scale: 10 = deep and refreshing

**Vitality factor in morning**  (scale 1= very tired, hungover, not well, dying)
(scale: 10 = full of energy, clear headed, refreshed, generally fantastic) ....................................................out of 10

## Breakfast

Time eaten: ............................................
Food:.........................................................................................................................................................
.................................................................................................................................................................

## Snack

Time eaten: ............................................
Food:.........................................................................................................................................................
.................................................................................................................................................................

## Lunch

Time eaten: ............................................
Food:.........................................................................................................................................................
.................................................................................................................................................................
.................................................................................................................................................................

## Snack

Time eaten: ............................................
Food:.........................................................................................................................................................
.................................................................................................................................................................

## Dinner

Time eaten: ............................................
Food:.........................................................................................................................................................
.................................................................................................................................................................
.................................................................................................................................................................

**Exercise**: .................................................................................................................................................
.................................................................................................................................................................

**Quality of day out of 10**...............................................................................................................................

NOTES AND OBSERVATIONS

. . . . . . . . . . . . . . . . . . . . . . . . . . .
. . . . . . . . . . . . . . . . . . . . . . . . . . .
. . . . . . . . . . . . . . . . . . . . . . . . . . .
. . . . . . . . . . . . . . . . . . . . . . . . . . .
. . . . . . . . . . . . . . . . . . . . . . . . . . .
. . . . . . . . . . . . . . . . . . . . . . . . . . .
. . . . . . . . . . . . . . . . . . . . . . . . . . .
. . . . . . . . . . . . . . . . . . . . . . . . . . .
. . . . . . . . . . . . . . . . . . . . . . . . . . .
. . . . . . . . . . . . . . . . . . . . . . . . . . .
. . . . . . . . . . . . . . . . . . . . . . . . . . .
. . . . . . . . . . . . . . . . . . . . . . . . . . .
. . . . . . . . . . . . . . . . . . . . . . . . . . .
. . . . . . . . . . . . . . . . . . . . . . . . . . .
. . . . . . . . . . . . . . . . . . . . . . . . . . .
. . . . . . . . . . . . . . . . . . . . . . . . . . .
. . . . . . . . . . . . . . . . . . . . . . . . . . .
. . . . . . . . . . . . . . . . . . . . . . . . . . .
. . . . . . . . . . . . . . . . . . . . . . . . . . .
. . . . . . . . . . . . . . . . . . . . . . . . . . .
. . . . . . . . . . . . . . . . . . . . . . . . . . .
. . . . . . . . . . . . . . . . . . . . . . . . . . .
. . . . . . . . . . . . . . . . . . . . . . . . . . .
. . . . . . . . . . . . . . . . . . . . . . . . . . .
. . . . . . . . . . . . . . . . . . . . . . . . . . .

# A-Z OF VITAL FOOD FACTS

**A is for...**

**Apples**

A medium size apple contains approximately 15 grams of carbohydrate or the equivalent of three teaspoons of white sugar! Unless you picked it a few days before you ate it, it will contain just a fraction of its original nutrients. Many supermarket fruit are up to 4 weeks old and may have been picked before they have ripened. It will have lost 70% of its vitamin content within a few days of being picked. You are mostly eating pure sugar with a little fibre. It is therefore not as healthy a snack as you have been led to believe. Always slow down the digestion of the sugar in fruit by eating it with a similar amount of protein, eg, 2oz/50g cheese or 2 slices of roast turkey. Never eat fruit on its own.

**Aspartame** ( Nutrasweet, Equal, Spoonful etc)

Very nasty and very poisonous. When the temperature of aspartame exceeds 86 degrees F. the wood alcohol in aspartame converts to formaldehyde and then to formic acid, which in turn causes metabolic acidosis and changes the brain's chemistry. The methanol toxicity mimics multiple sclerosis, thus many people are being wrongly diagnosed. Multiple Sclerosis is not a death sentence, whereas methanol toxicity is. Three to four cans of diet soda a day can trigger systemic lupus or multiple sclerosis symptoms. Aspartame makes you crave carbohydrates and makes you fat. I have seen people lose up to 20 pounds just coming off the

# DAY 4

**TODAYS DATE** ..........................................................................................................................................................................

**Quality of sleep:** ..................................**Number of hours slept**: ................................................................................

Scale: 1 = poor  Scale: 10 = deep and refreshing

**Vitality factor in morning**  (scale 1= very tired, hungover, not well, dying)

(scale: 10 = full of energy, clear headed, refreshed, generally fantastic) ..............................................................out of 10

**Breakfast**

Time eaten: ................................................

Food:........................................................................................................................................................................

..............................................................................................................................................................................

**Snack**

Time eaten: ................................................

Food:........................................................................................................................................................................

..............................................................................................................................................................................

**Lunch**

Time eaten: ................................................

Food:........................................................................................................................................................................

..............................................................................................................................................................................

..............................................................................................................................................................................

**Snack**

Time eaten: ................................................

Food:........................................................................................................................................................................

..............................................................................................................................................................................

**Dinner**

Time eaten: ................................................

Food:........................................................................................................................................................................

..............................................................................................................................................................................

..............................................................................................................................................................................

**Exercise**: ...............................................................................................................................................................

..............................................................................................................................................................................

**Quality of day out of 10**..........................................................................................................................................

diet soda and sweeteners. Aspartame is particularly deadly for diabetics. Avoid all 'diet', 'low sugar' or 'sugar free' foods, which contain it. (See Excitotoxins: The Taste that Kills by Dr. Russell Blaylock (Heath Press 1-800-643-2665)

## Almonds

The prince of nuts, nature's perfectly balanced highly nutritious snack. Best eaten plain or roasted, not salted. Contain equal amounts of protein and carbohydrate and a high level of good Omega 3 unsaturated fats. Their saturated fat content is only 10%. They are high in calories, which makes them ideal to make up your calorie allowance on a low starch diet but fattening if you eat too many. Limit a snack serving to a maximum of eight to ten nuts. They are chock full of calcium, magnesium and potassium. Cashew nuts are also similar, eat in small snack sizes of up to 8 nuts. A handful of 8 nuts a day will supply all your calcium needs to keep your bones healthy in a bio-absorpable form and is much more effective than taking a calcium suppliment.

## Addictions

Eating carbohydrates in excess, or using stimulants such as cigarettes, alcohol or recreational drugs causes the increase of insulin levels, which results in a rapid release of serotonin stored in the brain. This causes your mood to improve and for a short while you feel better. Then the insulin and serotonin drops quite quickly, leaving you feeling low and your brain demands more of the carbohydrate or drug to obtain another rush of serotonin. Using one stimulant leads to using another and addictions feed on each other. Eventually the store of serotonin in the brain is depleted and is unable to keep up with your need and no matter how many cigarettes you smoke, chocolate you eat or cups of coffee you drink, you cannot get the rush you have become dependent on. You are now serotonin depleted, which will leave you depressed. Regular small meals of adequate proteins, good fats, magnesium, calcium and B vitamins will help replenish the serotonin depletion and help you overcome your addictions. The amino acid L-Glutamine is also an excellent supplement to help stop cravings. Take up to 3000mg (1000mg x 3 daily) between meals on an empty stomach. Low oestrogen levels can also trigger low serotonin production and menopausal women may need natural hormonal help to alleviate the cravings.
See also Fish and Fish oils

NOTES AND OBSERVATIONS

# DAY 5

**TODAYS DATE**........................................................................................................................................

**Quality of sleep:**..........................**Number of hours slept**:........................................................
Scale: 1 = poor  Scale: 10 = deep and refreshing

**Vitality factor in morning** (scale 1= very tired, hungover, not well, dying)
(scale: 10 = full of energy, clear headed, refreshed, generally fantastic)..............................................out of 10

**Breakfast**

Time eaten:..........................................

Food:...................................................................................................................................

..........................................................................................................................................

**Snack**

Time eaten:..........................................

Food:...................................................................................................................................

..........................................................................................................................................

**Lunch**

Time eaten:..........................................

Food:...................................................................................................................................

..........................................................................................................................................

..........................................................................................................................................

**Snack**

Time eaten:..........................................

Food:...................................................................................................................................

..........................................................................................................................................

**Dinner**

Time eaten:..........................................

Food:...................................................................................................................................

..........................................................................................................................................

..........................................................................................................................................

**Exercise**:..........................................................................................................................

..........................................................................................................................................

**Quality of day out of 10**.....................................................................................................

**TODAYS DATE** ...................................................................................................................................................

**Quality of sleep:** ...........................................**Number of hours slept**: .......................................................
Scale: 1 = poor  Scale: 10 = deep and refreshing

**Vitality factor in morning** (scale 1= very tired, hungover, not well, dying)
(scale: 10 = full of energy, clear headed, refreshed, generally fantastic) ...................................................out of 10

**Breakfast**

Time eaten: ......................................

Food:...............................................................................................................................................................

.........................................................................................................................................................................

**Snack**

Time eaten: ......................................

Food:...............................................................................................................................................................

.........................................................................................................................................................................

**Lunch**

Time eaten: ......................................

Food:...............................................................................................................................................................

.........................................................................................................................................................................

.........................................................................................................................................................................

**Snack**

Time eaten: ......................................

Food:...............................................................................................................................................................

.........................................................................................................................................................................

**Dinner**

Time eaten: ......................................

Food:...............................................................................................................................................................

.........................................................................................................................................................................

.........................................................................................................................................................................

**Exercise**: ......................................................................................................................................................

.........................................................................................................................................................................

**Quality of day out of 10**..........................................................................................................................

# DAY 7

**TODAYS DATE** ...............................................................................................................................................................

**Quality of sleep:** .............................**Number of hours slept**: ...........................................................................
Scale: 1 = poor  Scale: 10 = deep and refreshing

**Vitality factor in morning** (scale 1= very tired, hungover, not well, dying)
(scale: 10 = full of energy, clear headed, refreshed, generally fantastic) ...........................................................out of 10

**Breakfast**

Time eaten: ...........................................
Food:.......................................................................................................................................................
.................................................................................................................................................................

**Snack**

Time eaten: ...........................................
Food:.......................................................................................................................................................
.................................................................................................................................................................

**Lunch**

Time eaten: ...........................................
Food:.......................................................................................................................................................
.................................................................................................................................................................
.................................................................................................................................................................

**Snack**

Time eaten: ...........................................
Food:.......................................................................................................................................................
.................................................................................................................................................................

**Dinner**

Time eaten: ...........................................
Food:.......................................................................................................................................................
.................................................................................................................................................................
.................................................................................................................................................................

**Exercise**: ...............................................................................................................................................
.................................................................................................................................................................

**Quality of day out of 10**...........................................................................................................................

15

## Acne

Approximately 20% of all cases of long-term adult acne I see are 100% food intolerances which have built up to a toxic level in the body. Occasionally they are caused by a food allergy but these causes will be noticed earlier by the sufferer. The most common cause of adult acne are parasites living in the sinuses or throat which can live for many years. Both food and parasite caused acne are aggravated by hormonal patterns which makes them appear to be hormonally caused. However, no amount of hormonal intervention or medication appears to have any long term effect. Food intolerance related acne tends to have a more rash like appearance around the chin. The sinuses are also often affected and give a constant runny nose and nasal drip. Parasite related acne are usually large, angry, painful spots often accompanied by headaches. For parasit information, please see my web sight - www.judycole.co.uk. If you suspect food as the cause, refer to the food intolerances for your blood type and eliminate these strictly for 2 months. If it is the food causing your skin condition, you will see the problem worsen and improve several times over the 2 months period before finally clearing up. I have many cases of strange foods causing acne which are not on the lists, such as lettuce or yeast but you will need to be individually tested to ascertain these by a specialised food kinesiologist. Avoid all yeast and fermented products regardless of your blood type. This includes all alcohol. I am also seeing increasing skin rashes and spots around the chin and forehead appearing as a direct result of skin creams, shampoos, shaving lotion and even toothpaste. These products all contain similar base chemicals which may have built up to a critical toxic level in your skin after many years of use, which out of the blue, will seem to suddenly trigger acne. Search out completely natural products from health shops and known herbal brands. You will need to use them for a minimum of six months to see an improvement as it will take this long for your skin to detox the chemical build up completely. It is good advice for everyone to go natural!

## WEIGH AND MEASURE DAY

weight...................... kgs/lbs
waist ............................. cm
hips ............................... cm
bust/chest ...................... cm
top of thigh..................... cm
top of arm ...................... cm
knee ............................. cm
calf............................... cm

### Weekly marks out of 10

Sleep quality ........................
Average no hours slept...........
AM vitality factor...................
Quality of week ....................
Adherence to programme.......
No of days exercised ............

### NOTES AND OBSERVATIONS

....................................................
....................................................
....................................................
....................................................
....................................................
....................................................

# DAY 8

**TODAYS DATE** .........................................................................................................................................................................

**Quality of sleep:** ................................**Number of hours slept**: ......................................................................................

Scale: 1 = poor  Scale: 10 = deep and refreshing

**Vitality factor in morning**  (scale 1= very tired, hungover, not well, dying)

(scale: 10 = full of energy, clear headed, refreshed, generally fantastic) ..........................................................................out of 10

**Breakfast**

Time eaten: ........................................

Food:.........................................................................................................................................................................

...........................................................................................................................................................................

**Snack**

Time eaten: ........................................

Food:.........................................................................................................................................................................

...........................................................................................................................................................................

**Lunch**

Time eaten: ........................................

Food:.........................................................................................................................................................................

...........................................................................................................................................................................

...........................................................................................................................................................................

**Snack**

Time eaten: ........................................

Food:.........................................................................................................................................................................

...........................................................................................................................................................................

**Dinner**

Time eaten: ........................................

Food:.........................................................................................................................................................................

...........................................................................................................................................................................

...........................................................................................................................................................................

**Exercise**: ...............................................................................................................................................................

...........................................................................................................................................................................

**Quality of day out of 10**............................................................................................................................................

## Arthritis

One of the most common complaints reported by clients of all ages are aches and pains in the joints and muscles, with an alarming increase in younger people in their twenties. The symptoms range from mild stiffness to full blown diagnosed rheumatoid arthritic symptoms of extreme pain and swelling. Food plays a causative role in as many as 80% of all the cases I have seen. Even if the main cause is parasitic, which many cases of arthritis are, the importance of avoiding certain food intolerances is always stressed by the body. These intolerances are those commonly associated with the blood type and require 2-5 months of strict elimination. Tea, coffee, tomatoes and yeast must always be avoided, regardless of blood group.

## Avocados

This wonderful fruit is an excellent source of good fat and cholesterol and is full of digestive enzymes. Although high in calories, in terms of nutrients per calorie they are a Superfood and two or three avocados a week in your salads are a great source of folic acid, B vitamins and potassium. They are an excellent source of dietary cholesterol,... enjoy them!

# DAY 9

**TODAYS DATE** ....................................................................................................................................................................................

**Quality of sleep:** .................................**Number of hours slept**: ...........................................................................................

Scale: 1 = poor  Scale: 10 = deep and refreshing

**Vitality factor in morning**  (scale 1= very tired, hungover, not well, dying)

(scale: 10 = full of energy, clear headed, refreshed, generally fantastic) ...............................................................................out of 10

**Breakfast**

Time eaten: ...........................................

Food:........................................................................................................................................................................................

..............................................................................................................................................................................................

**Snack**

Time eaten: ...........................................

Food:........................................................................................................................................................................................

..............................................................................................................................................................................................

**Lunch**

Time eaten: ...........................................

Food:........................................................................................................................................................................................

..............................................................................................................................................................................................

..............................................................................................................................................................................................

**Snack**

Time eaten: ...........................................

Food:........................................................................................................................................................................................

..............................................................................................................................................................................................

**Dinner**

Time eaten: ...........................................

Food:........................................................................................................................................................................................

..............................................................................................................................................................................................

..............................................................................................................................................................................................

**Exercise**: ...............................................................................................................................................................................

..............................................................................................................................................................................................

**Quality of day out of 10**............................................................................................................................................................

## B is for...

### Butter

A natural good saturated fat when eaten in moderation. Butter is an excellent food, full of nutrients and the shorter fats that are easiest for us to digest and burn as fuel. Even most lactose intolerant A Blood types can tolerate butter. The best alternatives available on the market are soft spreads made with olive oil. I have not found one other margarine on the market that the body has not consistently tested negatively to, which include all the major brands. Our bodies have evolved with butter over many years - do not be afraid to use it. Your body needs some natural saturated fats and it is far better to eat natural fats than man made ones. Butter is also the only fat which does not change its molecular structure when heated. As explained in The Body Talks Programme, all oils become dangerous and poisonous when heated and should not be used for any cooking. Ignore all the marketing on the benefits of cooking with oil, even olive oil. Return to nature and use a little butter. Your palate will love it and your heart will not suffer, quite the contrary.

### Bread

The two main components of bread are wheat and yeast, two of the most common food intolerances. If you are yeast intolerant, then all wheat free breads can also give you problems. My tests of over 2000 people show that around 98% of us are intolerant to modern day hybrid wheat, a form of wheat modified from original Spelt wheat over the last 130 years, through selective breeding and genetic modification. Wheat free breads, made with 100% rye flour or old-fashioned Spelt flour are becoming more readily available in health food shops and supermarkets. Also keep in mind that one slice of bread contains around 18 grams of starch carbohydrate. Most people need only around 30 grams of starch in the whole day. As Cindy Crawford is famously quoted as saying "You may as well just sit on it". Bread is fattening, period. If you are trying to lose weight, substitute Ryvita for bread and eat lots of low carbohydrate nutritious vegetables. Consign regular bread consumption to the past. Unless you are very physically active, eating bread will make weight control an ongoing battle.

NOTES AND OBSERVATIONS

# DAY 10

**TODAYS DATE** ...........................................................................................................................................................

**Quality of sleep:** ..................................**Number of hours slept**: ...........................................................................

Scale: 1 ⇒ poor  Scale: 10 = deep and refreshing

**Vitality factor in morning** (scale 1= very tired, hungover, not well, dying)

(scale: 10 = full of energy, clear headed, refreshed, generally fantastic) ...............................................................out of 10

## Breakfast

Time eaten: ....................................

Food:.........................................................................................................................................................

...........................................................................................................................................................

## Snack

Time eaten: ....................................

Food:.........................................................................................................................................................

...........................................................................................................................................................

## Lunch

Time eaten: ....................................

Food:.........................................................................................................................................................

...........................................................................................................................................................

...........................................................................................................................................................

## Snack

Time eaten: ....................................

Food:.........................................................................................................................................................

...........................................................................................................................................................

## Dinner

Time eaten: ....................................

Food:.........................................................................................................................................................

...........................................................................................................................................................

...........................................................................................................................................................

**Exercise**: ...................................................................................................................................................

...........................................................................................................................................................

**Quality of day out of 10**.............................................................................................................................

## Beer

Apart from the alcohol in it, beer consists of significant amounts of yeast and sugar. It is very fattening! One 12oz can of beer contains around 180 calories and 15grams of sugar (equivalent to 3 teaspoons of white sugar) which may not seem a lot considering an apple contains the same, but the alcohol is a 'SuperSugar' meaning it is absorbed the most rapidly of any sugars into the bloodstream. The more rapid the digestion of a sugar, the more body fat it makes. Alcohol is toxic to cells and also accelerates the ageing process.

The infamous beer belly is often a toxic pot of accumulated yeast intolerance, lovingly stored over many years. The body takes 5 days to detox the yeast from one beer, ensuring one beer every 5 days maintains a toxic build up. Only strict avoidance of all yeast containing foods, not just beer, for at least 4 months, will slowly see the belly soften and disappear, regardless of other diet regimes. Sorry guys...... Drink too much beer, get fat! Drink it in moderation.

## Back ache

For many years I worked with professional sports people as a remedial masseur, treating a wide range of injuries with deep remedial and Chinese massage techniques. I would spend hours working deep into the muscles to release spasm and pain. However, when I began asking the body what had been the underlying cause of the injury and understanding how energy lines in the body connect the internal organs to the muscles, a completely new picture unravelled. A majority, except true impact or fall injuries, were food related.

The large intestine meridian line used in Chinese medicine, also controls the energy flow and therefore strength or weakness of the hamstring and the lower back muscles. If your large intestine is being damaged by food intolerances, parasites or bacteria, the energy meridian becomes weak. The corresponding muscles also become weak, resulting in repetitive hamstring injury or chronic lower back pain. No amount of physiotherapy or massage treatment will compleatly re-strengthen this muscle. However, when the large intestine is treated, the majority of back and muscle problems miraculously disappear as the muscle responds to the energy flow. Food intolerances can also directly result in inflammation in the spine, particularly at points of previous injury or

NOTES AND OBSERVATIONS

# DAY 11

**TODAYS DATE** ...........................................................................................................................................................................

**Quality of sleep:** ...........................**Number of hours slept**: ...........................................................................................
Scale: 1 = poor  Scale: 10 = deep and refreshing

**Vitality factor in morning**  (scale 1= very tired, hungover, not well, dying)
(scale: 10 = full of energy, clear headed, refreshed, generally fantastic) .........................................................out of 10

**Breakfast**
Time eaten: ...........................................
Food:.......................................................................................................................................................................
..............................................................................................................................................................................

**Snack**
Time eaten: ...........................................
Food:.......................................................................................................................................................................
..............................................................................................................................................................................

**Lunch**
Time eaten: ...........................................
Food:.......................................................................................................................................................................
..............................................................................................................................................................................
..............................................................................................................................................................................

**Snack**
Time eaten: ...........................................
Food:.......................................................................................................................................................................
..............................................................................................................................................................................

**Dinner**
Time eaten: ...........................................
Food:.......................................................................................................................................................................
..............................................................................................................................................................................
..............................................................................................................................................................................

**Exercise**: ..............................................................................................................................................................
..............................................................................................................................................................................

**Quality of day out of 10**...........................................................................................................................................

degeneration. A 36 year old woman came to see me a week before she was scheduled for major back surgery for a diagnosed slipped disc. The pain in her lower back and down her legs had become unbearable and was no longer responding to the strongest pain-killers. Her body put the cause of the inflammatory pain at 100% intolerance to dairy products and tropical fruit, both of which she was eating regularly. She was keen to avoid surgery and agreed to put it off for one month. Within two weeks she began to see an improvement. Over the next 2 months the pain improved and she only needed a mild anti-inflammatory occasionally if she was standing for any length of time. She began to go to the gym four times weekly to strengthen the muscles around the disc. Eight months after starting the detox, she sometimes feels a slight ache first thing in the morning but no longer needed any pain killers. She never had an operation and two and a half years later is completely pain free as long as she exercises regularly. One day she ate a fruit cocktail drink which unbeknown to her, contained banana. The pain returned with a vengeance the next day and took 5 days to clear.

This underlying cause may be why so many back operations are not successful, even though the damage has been carefully and properly repaired during surgery. Unless those foods are eliminated, the inflammation persists around the weakened area and there is no relief.

I hate to think how many injuries in professional sportsmen have been caused at least in part, by the advocating of wheat pasta carbo loading before big events! Many muscular weaknesses are linked to foods. If you are a serious athlete, experiment by doing time trials with a small bag of wheat strapped to your waist. Just the negative energy field of the wheat near your body's energy field, is enough to weaken your muscle integrity enough to slow you down. Compare that to your normal times. If you are wheat intolerant which most of you will be, your times will, in athletic terms, be significantly slower with the wheat, giving you some idea of how this everyday food may be curbing your performance.

# DAY 12

**TODAYS DATE** ...................................................................................................................................................................................

**Quality of sleep:** ...............................**Number of hours slept**: .........................................................................................

Scale: 1 = poor  Scale: 10 = deep and refreshing

**Vitality factor in morning**  (scale 1= very tired, hungover, not well, dying)

(scale: 10 = full of energy, clear headed, refreshed, generally fantastic) ......................................................................out of 10

**Breakfast**

Time eaten: .......................................

Food:...................................................................................................................................................................................

......................................................................................................................................................................................

**Snack**

Time eaten: .......................................

Food:...................................................................................................................................................................................

......................................................................................................................................................................................

**Lunch**

Time eaten: .......................................

Food:...................................................................................................................................................................................

......................................................................................................................................................................................

......................................................................................................................................................................................

**Snack**

Time eaten: .......................................

Food:...................................................................................................................................................................................

......................................................................................................................................................................................

**Dinner**

Time eaten: .......................................

Food:...................................................................................................................................................................................

......................................................................................................................................................................................

......................................................................................................................................................................................

**Exercise**: ...........................................................................................................................................................................

......................................................................................................................................................................................

**Quality of day out of 10**.................................................................................................................................................

**TODAYS DATE** ............................................................................................................................................

**Quality of sleep:** ...................................**Number of hours slept**: ..........................................................
Scale: 1 = poor  Scale: 10 = deep and refreshing

**Vitality factor in morning**  (scale 1= very tired, hungover, not well, dying)
(scale: 10 = full of energy, clear headed, refreshed, generally fantastic) ...........................................out of 10

**Breakfast**
Time eaten: ............................................
Food:.......................................................................................................................................................
............................................................................................................................................................

**Snack**
Time eaten: ............................................
Food:.......................................................................................................................................................
............................................................................................................................................................

**Lunch**
Time eaten: ............................................
Food:.......................................................................................................................................................
............................................................................................................................................................
............................................................................................................................................................

**Snack**
Time eaten: ............................................
Food:.......................................................................................................................................................
............................................................................................................................................................

**Dinner**
Time eaten: ............................................
Food:.......................................................................................................................................................
............................................................................................................................................................
............................................................................................................................................................

**Exercise**: ............................................................................................................................................
............................................................................................................................................................
**Quality of day out of 10**...............................................................................................................................

# DAY 14

**TODAYS DATE** .................................................................................................................................

**Quality of sleep:** ...............................**Number of hours slept**: ...........................................................

Scale: 1 = poor   Scale: 10 = deep and refreshing

**Vitality factor in morning**  (scale 1= very tired, hungover, not well, dying)

(scale: 10 = full of energy, clear headed, refreshed, generally fantastic) ...........................................................out of 10

**Breakfast**

Time eaten: ...........................................

Food:...................................................................................................................................................

.............................................................................................................................................................

**Snack**

Time eaten: ...........................................

Food:...................................................................................................................................................

.............................................................................................................................................................

**Lunch**

Time eaten: ...........................................

Food:...................................................................................................................................................

.............................................................................................................................................................

.............................................................................................................................................................

**Snack**

Time eaten: ...........................................

Food:...................................................................................................................................................

.............................................................................................................................................................

**Dinner**

Time eaten: ...........................................

Food:...................................................................................................................................................

.............................................................................................................................................................

.............................................................................................................................................................

**Exercise**: ...........................................................................................................................................

.............................................................................................................................................................

**Quality of day out of 10**...............................................................................................................

## Breakfast

The most important meal of the day. Your body has gone twelve hours overnight since dinner without protein, albeit not using much during sleep, but at around 7am your metabolic rate wakes up and begins to use protein. If you don't eat it at breakfast, you are going as long as seventeen hours since the previous night's meal without that vital protein refill. In addition to this a good breakfast stimulates your metabolic rate and you will burn off an additional 15% of calories during the day. A breakfast with equal amounts of protein, carbohydrates and fat balances your blood sugar level and brain chemistry and ensures that you don't get cravings by mid morning. If you miss breakfast your sugar levels and brain chemistry play catch up all day.

## Burgers

If caught out with nothing to eat, a burger with the bun taken off, a few chips (if you really must) and a salad will do the job of filling you up nicely without doing too much damage to your diet. Of course for the meat eaters a homemade steak mince burger with a large salad is a delicious meal. Fast food burgers do carry the risk of poor quality meat and extra fat. Be choosy and only eat them in emergency.

**WEIGH AND MEASURE DAY**

weight...................... kgs/lbs
waist ............................. cm
hips ............................... cm
bust/chest ....................... cm
top of thigh..................... cm
top of arm ...................... cm
knee .............................. cm
calf................................ cm

### Weekly marks out of 10
Sleep quality ........................
Average no hours slept...........
AM vitality factor ...................
Quality of week ....................
Adherence to programme.......
No of days exercised ...........

### NOTES AND OBSERVATIONS
.................................................
.................................................
.................................................
.................................................
.................................................
.................................................

# DAY 15

**TODAYS DATE** ...................................................................................................................................................

**Quality of sleep:** ...............................**Number of hours slept**: ...................................................................

Scale: 1 = poor  Scale: 10 = deep and refreshing

**Vitality factor in morning**  (scale 1= very tired, hungover, not well, dying)

(scale: 10 = full of energy, clear headed, refreshed, generally fantastic) ...................................................out of 10

**Breakfast**

Time eaten: ...........................................

Food:.............................................................................................................................................................

.......................................................................................................................................................................

**Snack**

Time eaten: ...........................................

Food:.............................................................................................................................................................

.......................................................................................................................................................................

**Lunch**

Time eaten: ...........................................

Food:.............................................................................................................................................................

.......................................................................................................................................................................

.......................................................................................................................................................................

**Snack**

Time eaten: ...........................................

Food:.............................................................................................................................................................

.......................................................................................................................................................................

**Dinner**

Time eaten: ...........................................

Food:.............................................................................................................................................................

.......................................................................................................................................................................

.......................................................................................................................................................................

**Exercise**: ....................................................................................................................................................

.......................................................................................................................................................................

**Quality of day out of 10**.............................................................................................................................

## C is for...

### Calcium

Calcium is essential for many body functions, including regulation of the heartbeat, conduction of nerve impulses, stimulation of hormone secretions and clotting of blood, as well as for building and maintaining a healthy skeleton. Calcium is a mineral found in many foods and adequate calcium intake is important because the human body cannot produce calcium. Even after reaching full skeletal growth, adequate calcium intake is important because the body loses calcium every day through shed skin, nails, hair and sweat as well as through urine and faeces. This lost calcium must be replaced daily through the diet. When the diet does not contain enough calcium to perform these activities, calcium is taken from the bones, the storage area for calcium.

Calcium is the most abundant mineral in the body. To be absorbed properly into the bones and teeth, calcium must be accompanied by magnesium and phosphorous in a minimum ratio of 2 calcium to 1 magnesium/phosphorous as well as vitamins A, C, D and E. In addition to this necessary balance of nutrients, calcium is only fully digested and absorbed in the presence of bile, the enzyme released by the liver to digest fats. For example, fully skimmed milk, which is almost totally fat free, does not trigger bile to be released into the body when the milk is drunk, thereby making it indigestible and preventing absorption of its calcium. Very low fat diets are a major, unrecognised contributor to low calcium absorption and potential osteoporosis, the development of porous bones. This need for a high bile release into the stomach to absorb many nutrients also highlights the difficulty the body has in digesting and absorbing calcium supplements when taken with a low fat meal. It is worth noting that most of us take supplements with breakfast which for many has become a low fat, high carbohydrate meal. By eating the balanced breakfasts suggested on The Body Talks Programme, all the supplements you might be taking will be properly absorbed.

If calcium is not properly digested and absorbed, the tablet dissolves and is passed into the blood where it eventually deposits as calcium spurs in the joints, on the surface of some bones and also in the kidney and liver. The body

NOTES AND OBSERVATIONS

# DAY 16

**TODAYS DATE** ....................................................................................................................................................................

**Quality of sleep:** .................................**Number of hours slept**: ............................................................................

Scale: 1 = poor  Scale: 10 = deep and refreshing

**Vitality factor in morning**  (scale 1= very tired, hungover, not well, dying)

(scale: 10 = full of energy, clear headed, refreshed, generally fantastic) ...............................................out of 10

**Breakfast**

Time eaten: .........................................

Food:....................................................................................................................................................................

............................................................................................................................................................................

**Snack**

Time eaten: .........................................

Food:....................................................................................................................................................................

............................................................................................................................................................................

**Lunch**

Time eaten: .........................................

Food:....................................................................................................................................................................

............................................................................................................................................................................

............................................................................................................................................................................

**Snack**

Time eaten: .........................................

Food:....................................................................................................................................................................

............................................................................................................................................................................

**Dinner**

Time eaten: .........................................

Food:....................................................................................................................................................................

............................................................................................................................................................................

............................................................................................................................................................................

**Exercise**: ..........................................................................................................................................................

............................................................................................................................................................................

**Quality of day out of 10**..................................................................................................................................

explained this to me after I noticed that many of my female patients between the ages of 40 and 60 were complaining of stiff joints. All of them, bar none, had been taking calcium supplements for three months or more, to help prevent osteoporosis. In fact the supplements were not effective in preventing osteoporosis, but had actually caused the stiff joints and in some cases frozen shoulders. When they were taken off the calcium supplement, all of them found their joints and stiffness improving within 2 months. Of the 2000 odd clients I have seen, not one body has ever requested a simple calcium supplement. To increase their calcium intake the body suggested almonds as the best supplement form. 8-10 almonds a day will more than supplement your calcium requirements and are perfectly balanced with the full spectrum of required minerals. They also contain fat to ensure the release of bile. People often ask me about where they can get calcium from if I find through testing for food intolerances that they are intolerant to lactose and cannot eat dairy. On closer questioning, their bodies told me that people who are lactose intolerant have never been able to absorb calcium from milk and many dairy products anyway. They have always got their calcium from other foods and by eating a high dairy diet, to obtain calcium, were actually not eating enough of the foods that actually provide it to them. Research revealed an article in Reuters Health on June 27, 2003 as follows.

**NEW YORK** (Reuters Health) - People who are lactose intolerant – meaning they cannot digest dairy products – tend to get less calcium in their diets than others, and are therefore at risk of the bone-thinning disease osteoporosis, new research suggests.

Middle East researchers surveyed 66 men and women who were lactose intolerant and found that they took in an average of less than 700 milligrams of calcium each day, at least 300 milligrams less than the recommended dietary allowance (RDA) for adults.

In addition, bone scans revealed that lactose intolerant men and women who had reached menopause had thinning in certain parts of their skeletons not seen in people who digested dairy with ease.
Almost one-fifth of lactose intolerant people also had relatively high levels of the calcium-regulating parathyroid hormone (PTH). Too much PTH can cause calcium

## NOTES AND OBSERVATIONS

......................................
......................................
......................................
......................................
......................................
......................................
......................................
......................................
......................................
......................................
......................................
......................................
......................................
......................................
......................................
......................................
......................................
......................................
......................................
......................................
......................................
......................................
......................................
......................................
......................................
......................................
......................................
......................................
......................................
......................................
......................................
......................................
......................................

# DAY 17

**TODAYS DATE** ......................................................................................................................................................

**Quality of sleep:** ...................................**Number of hours slept**: ...........................................................

Scale: 1 = poor  Scale: 10 = deep and refreshing

**Vitality factor in morning**  (scale 1= very tired, hungover, not well, dying)

(scale: 10 = full of energy, clear headed, refreshed, generally fantastic) ....................................................out of 10

**Breakfast**

Time eaten: ...........................................

Food:......................................................................................................................................................

..............................................................................................................................................................

**Snack**

Time eaten: ...........................................

Food:......................................................................................................................................................

..............................................................................................................................................................

**Lunch**

Time eaten: ...........................................

Food:......................................................................................................................................................

..............................................................................................................................................................

..............................................................................................................................................................

**Snack**

Time eaten: ...........................................

Food:......................................................................................................................................................

..............................................................................................................................................................

**Dinner**

Time eaten: ...........................................

Food:......................................................................................................................................................

..............................................................................................................................................................

..............................................................................................................................................................

**Exercise**: ..............................................................................................................................................

..............................................................................................................................................................

**Quality of day out of 10**...........................................................................................................................

in bones to dissolve into the blood stream, weakening the bones and making them more susceptible to fracture.

"Patients with lactose intolerance have low calcium intake and consequently are more prone to osteoporosis," study author Dr. Sophia Ish-Shalom of Rambam Medical Center in Haifa told Reuters Health.

**SOURCE:** Journal of the American College of Nutrition 2003; 22:201-207.

If you are lactose intolerant it is vital that you follow a varied, balanced nutritious diet that includes plenty of calcium rich foods. Calcium, phosphorous and potassium can be found in plentiful supply in corn, dark rye, spelt, millet, wild rice, oats, eggs, meat, shellfish, green leafy vegetables, nuts, seeds and pulses.

If you are suffering therefore from the early stages of osteoporosis, one possible contributing cause could be an imbalance in your intake of magnesium, phosphorous and other vitamins combined with a dangerous low fat diet. It could also be, and this is what bodies are indicating to me, an insufficient intake of high quality proteins in your diet over a long period of time. Strong bones are made of protein. When women are told that their bones are thinning due to lack of calcium, this condition is called Osteomylecia... not osteoporosis. Most have a combination of the two. Good bone mass is a complex combination of sufficient protein in the diet to maintain the osteoblasts which make up bone, a good hormone level, as low oestrogen levels will reduce bone mass, and regular weight bearing exercise which stresses the bones and encourages them to build up osteoblasts and download the calcium to strengthen up the gaps between the osteoblasts in the bones. See Osteoporosis (page 106) for further information in preventing the condition.

● If you do take a calcium supplement ensure that it is in the form of Calcium Carbonate only. It is best taken with a combination of vitamin D, magnesium, zinc, potassium and phophorous, but this is difficult to find.

In three recent cases of ostioporosis, their bodies highlighted a genetic low liver enzyme responsible for calcium absorption.

## NOTES AND OBSERVATIONS

**TODAYS DATE** ...........................................................................................................................................................................

**Quality of sleep:** ...............................**Number of hours slept**: ...............................................................................

Scale: 1 = poor  Scale: 10 = deep and refreshing

**Vitality factor in morning** (scale 1= very tired, hungover, not well, dying)

(scale: 10 = full of energy, clear headed, refreshed, generally fantastic) .................................................................out of 10

**Breakfast**

Time eaten: ...........................................

Food:...............................................................................................................................................................

...........................................................................................................................................................................

**Snack**

Time eaten: ...........................................

Food:...............................................................................................................................................................

...........................................................................................................................................................................

**Lunch**

Time eaten: ...........................................

Food:...............................................................................................................................................................

...........................................................................................................................................................................

...........................................................................................................................................................................

**Snack**

Time eaten: ...........................................

Food:...............................................................................................................................................................

...........................................................................................................................................................................

**Dinner**

Time eaten: ...........................................

Food:...............................................................................................................................................................

...........................................................................................................................................................................

...........................................................................................................................................................................

**Exercise**: ....................................................................................................................................................

...........................................................................................................................................................................

**Quality of day out of 10**............................................................................................................................

## Carrots

Raw carrots are low in starch and can be eaten virtually unlimited. Cooked carrots however do turn starchy and there are 15 grams of starch in half a cup. Carrots are a healthy snack, and when eaten with humus as a dip, are a good balance of carbohydrate, protein and fat. They contain high levels of vitamin A and minerals such as potassium and selenium.

## Canderel

See Aspartame

## Cravings

See Addictions

## Cheating

This is going to happen. Hopefully not too much, if ever, in your first two months of serious repair detox. A tiny bit of an intolerant food will halt the whole detox process for five days until the blood is completely clear of it again. Even weekly cheating will therefore prolong your eventual clean up indefinitely. This is often why people don't think they eat enough of a food to cause any of their ill health. It takes only a little bread or cheese every 5 days to maintain a skin, sinus, tummy or similar food intolerance condition. Nobody said this was going to be easy. But the pay off for being really strict with yourself is enormous. Too many of my clients only do the programme 80%, get some results but do not see the break through into a complete alleviation of symptoms, only achieved by 100% adherence to the programme for at least 2 months. Then they conveniently blame the programme and never give themselves a chance to achieve super health.

In the long-term your food intolerances are not a life sentence (or should that be death sentence?). It is more a matter of finding out by trial and error how often you can cheat on a certain food intolerance without getting any adverse reactions. Some foods will immediately affect you, a test you can only truly undertake once your system has been completely cleared after a 2 month strict detox. Other foods will build up insidiously in your system without any physical warnings if eaten too regularly, until one day, six to twelve months later, you slowly realize you are back where you started and are feeling lethargic and bloated again. Then the only

.......................................
.......................................
.......................................
.......................................
.......................................
.......................................
.......................................
.......................................
.......................................
.......................................
.......................................
.......................................
.......................................
.......................................
.......................................
.......................................
.......................................
.......................................
.......................................
.......................................
.......................................
.......................................
.......................................
.......................................
.......................................
.......................................
.......................................

# DAY 19

**TODAYS DATE** ...............................................................................................................................................................................

**Quality of sleep:** ..................................**Number of hours slept**: ..........................................................................
Scale: 1 = poor  Scale: 10 = deep and refreshing

**Vitality factor in morning** (scale 1= very tired, hungover, not well, dying)
(scale: 10 = full of energy, clear headed, refreshed, generally fantastic) .............................................................out of 10

**Breakfast**

Time eaten: .........................................
Food:................................................................................................................................................................
.........................................................................................................................................................................

**Snack**

Time eaten: .........................................
Food:................................................................................................................................................................
.........................................................................................................................................................................

**Lunch**

Time eaten: .........................................
Food:................................................................................................................................................................
.........................................................................................................................................................................
.........................................................................................................................................................................

**Snack**

Time eaten: .........................................
Food:................................................................................................................................................................
.........................................................................................................................................................................

**Dinner**

Time eaten: .........................................
Food:................................................................................................................................................................
.........................................................................................................................................................................
.........................................................................................................................................................................

**Exercise**: ........................................................................................................................................................
.........................................................................................................................................................................
**Quality of day out of 10**.................................................................................................................................

**TODAYS DATE** .......................................................................................................................................................................

**Quality of sleep:** ...................................**Number of hours slept**: ...............................................................................
Scale: 1 = poor  Scale: 10 = deep and refreshing

**Vitality factor in morning** (scale 1= very tired, hungover, not well, dying)
(scale: 10 = full of energy, clear headed, refreshed, generally fantastic) .............................................................................out of 10

**Breakfast**
Time eaten: ...........................................
Food:...................................................................................................................................................................
.............................................................................................................................................................................

**Snack**
Time eaten: ...........................................
Food:...................................................................................................................................................................
.............................................................................................................................................................................

**Lunch**
Time eaten: ...........................................
Food:...................................................................................................................................................................
.............................................................................................................................................................................
.............................................................................................................................................................................

**Snack**
Time eaten: ...........................................
Food:...................................................................................................................................................................
.............................................................................................................................................................................

**Dinner**
Time eaten: ...........................................
Food:...................................................................................................................................................................
.............................................................................................................................................................................
.............................................................................................................................................................................

**Exercise**: ...........................................................................................................................................................................

**Quality of day out of 10**.................................................................................................................................................

# DAY 21

**TODAYS DATE** ...................................................................................................................................................................................

**Quality of sleep:** ................................................**Number of hours slept**: .............................................................................

Scale: 1 = poor  Scale: 10 = deep and refreshing

**Vitality factor in morning**  (scale 1= very tired, hungover, not well, dying)

(scale: 10 = full of energy, clear headed, refreshed, generally fantastic) ...................................................................out of 10

**Breakfast**

Time eaten: ...........................................

Food:........................................................................................................................................................................................

...............................................................................................................................................................................................

**Snack**

Time eaten: ...........................................

Food:........................................................................................................................................................................................

...............................................................................................................................................................................................

**Lunch**

Time eaten: ...........................................

Food:........................................................................................................................................................................................

...............................................................................................................................................................................................

...............................................................................................................................................................................................

**Snack**

Time eaten: ...........................................

Food:........................................................................................................................................................................................

...............................................................................................................................................................................................

**Dinner**

Time eaten: ...........................................

Food:........................................................................................................................................................................................

...............................................................................................................................................................................................

...............................................................................................................................................................................................

**Exercise**: .............................................................................................................................................................................

...............................................................................................................................................................................................

**Quality of day out of 10**...................................................................................................................................................

relief is another two month cellular detox and to start the programme again. For some of you, repeating the detox once a year will at least keep your health at a certain level and stop it getting increasingly worse, even if you do not follow it the rest of the year. For others, once you have tasted good health, the price of feeling dopey, irritable, sick, headachy or tummy pain for a piece of toast, is too high.

## Coffee

The 'O' and 'B' blood groups are intolerant to a protein in the coffee bean, not the caffeine. They may also be caffeine intolerant but that is separate, hence decaffeinated coffee is not the answer. If you are a heavy coffee drinker of around five or more cups a day, cut down slowly over the first week and then go cold turkey. If you drink under five cups a day, cut it out immediately. You will suffer from a couple of days of bad headaches, but drink lots of water and take a mild painkiller if desperate. The idea is to trigger a cellular clean out from the cells of old coffee toxic residue, which cannot happen if you are drinking even one coffee every five days. The 'A' blood type actually likes and thrives on coffee but limit your intake to no more than three a day, without milk of course and with only one sugar maximum. Try cream or goat's milk instead of cow's milk.

Coffee alternatives are limited to dandelion coffee and chicory, the latter of which may also be a food intolerance for some people. Your taste buds are your best guide.

## Crisps (Chips)

Most makes of crisp are high carbohydrate, high fat snacks which must be respected and eaten in moderation. Remember they are fried in hydrogenated oil, which automatically makes them very 'poisonous'. Choose your brand carefully and read the labels, some of them contain modified starch, a form of wheat. Try and choose the most natural makes which do not contain as many preservatives and food colourings. One of the healthier options are Hula Hoops which contain no wheat and are actually quite low in carbohydrates. Occasionally a bag of these with 2 oz of cold meat is a fairly acceptable quick snack. Tortilla corn chips are also a good option.

**WEIGH AND MEASURE DAY**

weight...................... kgs/lbs
waist ............................... cm
hips ................................. cm
bust/chest ...................... cm
top of thigh..................... cm
top of arm ...................... cm
knee .............................. cm
calf................................ cm

## Weekly marks out of 10

Sleep quality ........................
Average no hours slept...........
AM vitality factor...................
Quality of week ....................
Adherence to programme.......
No of days exercised ...........

NOTES AND OBSERVATIONS
.............................................
.............................................
.............................................
.............................................
.............................................
.............................................

# DAY 22

**TODAYS DATE** ...........................................................................................................................................................................................

**Quality of sleep:** ...................................**Number of hours slept**: ....................................................................................................

Scale: 1 = poor  Scale: 10 = deep and refreshing

**Vitality factor in morning**  (scale 1= very tired, hungover, not well, dying)

(scale: 10 = full of energy, clear headed, refreshed, generally fantastic) .....................................................................out of 10

**Breakfast**

Time eaten: ......................................

Food:.......................................................................................................................................................................................

.................................................................................................................................................................................................

**Snack**

Time eaten: ......................................

Food:.......................................................................................................................................................................................

.................................................................................................................................................................................................

**Lunch**

Time eaten: ......................................

Food:.......................................................................................................................................................................................

.................................................................................................................................................................................................

.................................................................................................................................................................................................

**Snack**

Time eaten: ......................................

Food:.......................................................................................................................................................................................

.................................................................................................................................................................................................

**Dinner**

Time eaten: ......................................

Food:.......................................................................................................................................................................................

.................................................................................................................................................................................................

.................................................................................................................................................................................................

**Exercise**: .............................................................................................................................................................................

.................................................................................................................................................................................................

**Quality of day out of 10**............................................................................................................................................................

## Cheese

If you are not intolerant to cows milk then cheese in moderation is an excellent source of protein, calcium and magnesium. If you are intolerant to lactose then most cheeses contain high amounts of lactose and will create excess mucous in your intestines when you eat them. Cheeses which are lower in lactose, are made with a higher whey or protein content such as Mozzarella, Feta and Halloumi, a cheese developed in Cyprus, which contains virtually no lactose and is predominantly made from Ewe's milk. Both these cheeses are also lower in saturated fat than cheddars, soft and cream cheeses. Avoid highly coloured and processed cheeses. 1oz/25g of cheese contains 8-10 grams of protein.

## Chemicals

We live in a chemical world. Chemicals have played a major role both in increasing our standard of living in the last 100 years and in destroying our precious planet and our health. Levels of chemical residue in our bodies are now alarmingly high, to the extent that corpses are now decomposing much slower! Cancer will continue to increase to epidemic proportions, I fear, until we recognise the part chemicals play in inducing it.

Meanwhile, you can help yourself by becoming aware of where they are to be found in the highest concentrations. Many people are unaware of the chemicals used in skin lotions, shampoos, body products, detergents and household cleaners. We use these products daily and tiny amounts of chemicals are being absorbed through the skin or inhaled each day, slowly building up to a toxic level in our bodies. All of these products, including some of the more expensive beauty products and creams, come up regularly as a major contributing cause in allergies, skin disorders and rashes, eczema, aches and pains, headaches and as a contributing factor to cancer. Switch to natural products, especially for skin and hair products, and where possible, household detergents, particularly washing-up liquid. Ask in your local health food shop for natural alternatives. The best shampoo I have found that is easily available and has little allergy reaction for most people, although it does contain SLS, is the Body Shop Ginger Shampoo. Please never discontinue this wonderful product Body Shop!

Deodorants can be particularly harmful as they are absorbed through the

## NOTES AND OBSERVATIONS

# DAY 23

**TODAYS DATE** .................................................................................................................................................................................

**Quality of sleep:** ................................**Number of hours slept**: ..............................................................................................

Scale: 1 = poor  Scale: 10 = deep and refreshing

**Vitality factor in morning**  (scale 1= very tired, hungover, not well, dying)

(scale: 10 = full of energy, clear headed, refreshed, generally fantastic) .........................................................................out of 10

**Breakfast**

Time eaten: .........................................

Food:................................................................................................................................................................................

.........................................................................................................................................................................................

**Snack**

Time eaten: .........................................

Food:................................................................................................................................................................................

.........................................................................................................................................................................................

**Lunch**

Time eaten: .........................................

Food:................................................................................................................................................................................

.........................................................................................................................................................................................

.........................................................................................................................................................................................

**Snack**

Time eaten: .........................................

Food:................................................................................................................................................................................

.........................................................................................................................................................................................

**Dinner**

Time eaten: .........................................

Food:................................................................................................................................................................................

.........................................................................................................................................................................................

.........................................................................................................................................................................................

**Exercise**: ..........................................................................................................................................................................

.........................................................................................................................................................................................

**Quality of day out of 10**.................................................................................................................................................

underarms into the lymphatic system and repeated use builds up toxic residue. The body has cited this buildup as a cause of breast cancer, as the body, in its infinite wisdom, attempts to channel the toxins away from vital organs to an area that even if removed, does not ultimately threaten life. In this instance, breast cancer may be a better option, but prevention is much, much better than the cure. Avoid chemical deodorants and use natural crystal, aluminium free or herbal products.

Chemicals in foods are also on the increase as foods need to have a longer shelf life or have extra flavourings and colourings added to meet an ever-increasing taste for more salty, sugary, stronger flavoured food. By reading labels and becoming aware of what is added to foods, you will be able to make the best choices available to you with what you are offered. Ideally, cook for yourself using raw natural products but we will never be able to avoid all chemicals; it is possibly too late for that in the current world, but vote with your feet and buy organic or natural whenever you can. Become a conscious consumer; do not believe anything you read about new man-made foods or products that stand to make multinationals big profits. Become knowledgeable about the way food is produced. It may save your life. It will help the future of our planet and the choices our children have to eat natural food.

### Chicken

Every 'B' Blood type I have tested and about 10% of 'A' blood types are highly intolerant to chicken. According to Dr Peter D'Adamo, author of the best selling "Eat Right For Your Type". A protein in chicken causes severe blood clotting in the 'B' blood group which highly increases your chances of a stroke. Chicken was the major cause of my multiple sclerosis symptoms and that of many other sufferers of this debilitating disease, according to their bodies when I have asked them. I made a full recovery after four years and other sufferers are feeling better since eliminating it from their diet. I only have to eat it twice in a week for the numbness to reoccur in my left toes.

The intensive farming methods of producing chicken has led to very high use of antibiotics and hormones in the feed, which naturally get passed into the bird and subsequently on to us. This is definitely one meat where free range or organic is worth the price if you eat a lot of it. Turkey is a better option. It is similar to chicken

NOTES AND OBSERVATIONS

....................................
....................................
....................................
....................................
....................................
....................................
....................................
....................................
....................................
....................................
....................................
....................................
....................................
....................................
....................................
....................................
....................................
....................................
....................................
....................................
....................................
....................................
....................................
....................................
....................................
....................................
....................................
....................................
....................................
....................................

DAY 24

**TODAYS DATE** ..............................................................................................................................................................

**Quality of sleep:** ................................**Number of hours slept**: ..................................................................................
Scale: 1 = poor  Scale: 10 = deep and refreshing

**Vitality factor in morning** (scale 1= very tired, hungover, not well, dying)
(scale: 10 = full of energy, clear headed, refreshed, generally fantastic) ...................................................................out of 10

**Breakfast**

Time eaten: ...........................................

Food:.........................................................................................................................................................................

................................................................................................................................................................................

**Snack**

Time eaten: ...........................................

Food:.........................................................................................................................................................................

................................................................................................................................................................................

**Lunch**

Time eaten: ...........................................

Food:.........................................................................................................................................................................

................................................................................................................................................................................

................................................................................................................................................................................

**Snack**

Time eaten: ...........................................

Food:.........................................................................................................................................................................

................................................................................................................................................................................

**Dinner**

Time eaten: ...........................................

Food:.........................................................................................................................................................................

................................................................................................................................................................................

................................................................................................................................................................................

**Exercise**: ...............................................................................................................................................................

................................................................................................................................................................................

**Quality of day out of 10**...............................................................................................................................................

in most respects but does not contain the dangerous proteins. They are also quite intensively farmed however, and also contain antibiotics and hormones.

**Constipation**

This is possibly one of the hardest conditions I treat. And one of the most common. Frequent underlying causes I have found through asking the body are bacteria in the large intestine, food intolerances and parasites. Unfortunately, even once the cause is eliminated, the damage done over many years leaves the natural peristaltic movement of the intestine, which moves the food through the body, weakened and lazy. It takes on average a minimum of five months to achieve any kind of normal bowel movement in most cases.

In total opposition to the established rule that constipation should be treated with extra fibre, particularly bran and raw veggies, the body repeatedly requests that you reduce the intake of raw fibre if the bowels are blocked and eat more soft baby type foods such as well cooked vegetables, soft fruits, yoghurt, soups and such. A large bowl of cooked vegetables daily is full of fibre but is easy to digest. If there is inflammation or irritable bowel syndrome present, which is the case nine times out of ten, the fibre found in whole grains, raw salads, raw vegetables and unpeeled fruits, can act like a scouring pad against the raw flesh, aggravating a very sensitive intestinal wall. Many cases of food intolerance related constipation are entirely due to our old friend, modern hybrid wheat. Often just avoiding foods containing wheat gives rapid relief. The results of this low fibre approach speak for themselves. Wheat is also a major cause of haemorrhoids, which magically clear up after a few months when wheat is eliminated from the diet. Try it, it may work for you. The Body Talks programme includes plenty of good fibre in your diet to maintain a healthy bowel function as long as you are eating plenty of salads, vegetables, nuts and seeds. Regular exercise and plenty of water are essential for healthy bowels.

The most powerful, effective and natural laxative for anyone suffering with chronic constipation is a tiny matchhead amount of the bitter crystal made from the Aloe Ferox Cactus. Studies in Germany have shown it outperfroms every other natural and allopathic alternative on the market and has no side effects, even when used for many years. Available to order on my website at www.judycole.co.uk

A less common but distressing detox symptom of avoiding your food intolerances

NOTES AND OBSERVATIONS

46

# DAY 25

**TODAYS DATE** .......................................................................................................................................................................

**Quality of sleep:** .....................................**Number of hours slept**: .....................................................................................

Scale: 1 = poor  Scale: 10 = deep and refreshing

**Vitality factor in morning**  (scale 1= very tired, hungover, not well, dying)

(scale: 10 = full of energy, clear headed, refreshed, generally fantastic) ...............................................................out of 10

**Breakfast**

Time eaten: ............................................

Food:.................................................................................................................................................................

............................................................................................................................................................................

**Snack**

Time eaten: ............................................

Food:.................................................................................................................................................................

............................................................................................................................................................................

**Lunch**

Time eaten: ............................................

Food:.................................................................................................................................................................

............................................................................................................................................................................

............................................................................................................................................................................

**Snack**

Time eaten: ............................................

Food:.................................................................................................................................................................

............................................................................................................................................................................

**Dinner**

Time eaten: ............................................

Food:.................................................................................................................................................................

............................................................................................................................................................................

............................................................................................................................................................................

**Exercise**: .............................................................................................................................................................

............................................................................................................................................................................

**Quality of day out of 10**...........................................................................................................................................

is the development of constipation. Unbeknown to you, your food intolerance may have had a loosening affect on your bowels over many years, causing the natural bowel peristaltic movement of the small and large intestine to become lazy. When these foods are naturally eliminated that diarrhoea affect is removed, and the lazy bowels may take several weeks to six months to begin to work normally. **Do not add fibre**, by resorting to softer, well cooked vegetables and fruit, the weakened bowel will slowly recover. Psillium husks and/or senecca will aid the movement. Drink plenty of water and be patient. The opposite affect often occurs if you have suffered with constipation before you start the elimination. Food intolerances, particularly wheat, can paralyse the gut but it quickly begins to work once the culprits are avoided

## Cream

Cream is the fat content of milk and as long as it is pure cream, not half and half, does not contain significant levels of either protein or lactose, making it tolerable in moderation for most people who are intolerant to milk. As cream is a fat, it can only be turned to body fat when eaten with sugars, for example cream and fruit, or cream and pasta. When eaten with protein or very low starch vegetables it is fine. It makes a useful base for meat sauces or to thicken vegetable soups such as broccoli or mushroom without being converted to body fat. Eat bread with the soup, however, and a different story ensues as the insulin is released in response to the carbohydrate, which then traps the cream as body fat in your cells. Remember, it is very high in saturated fat, calories and cholesterol and should be used respectfully and moderately.

## Corn

This delicious grain is very high in starch and sugars. One medium cob of corn contains around 30 grams of starch, 5 grams of protein and 130 calories. Do not think of sweet corn as a diet food! It may be low in fat but it is very fattening. A small amount of corn flour is the best alternative to wheat flour for thickening sauces if you are intolerant to wheat. It is also a very concentrated starch and should be used sparingly.

Corn and maize are also being extensively genetically modified which I suspect will lead to greater levels of intolerance in the future.

See popcorn.

NOTES AND OBSERVATIONS

# DAY 26

**TODAYS DATE** ................................................................................................................................................................

**Quality of sleep:** ...............................**Number of hours slept**: ........................................................................

Scale: 1 = poor  Scale: 10 = deep and refreshing

**Vitality factor in morning** (scale 1= very tired, hungover, not well, dying)

(scale: 10 = full of energy, clear headed, refreshed, generally fantastic) ...........................................................out of 10

**Breakfast**

Time eaten: ...........................................

Food:.....................................................................................................................................................................

............................................................................................................................................................................

**Snack**

Time eaten: ...........................................

Food:.....................................................................................................................................................................

............................................................................................................................................................................

**Lunch**

Time eaten: ...........................................

Food:.....................................................................................................................................................................

............................................................................................................................................................................

............................................................................................................................................................................

**Snack**

Time eaten: ...........................................

Food:.....................................................................................................................................................................

............................................................................................................................................................................

**Dinner**

Time eaten: ...........................................

Food:.....................................................................................................................................................................

............................................................................................................................................................................

............................................................................................................................................................................

**Exercise**: ...........................................................................................................................................................

............................................................................................................................................................................

**Quality of day out of 10**............................................................................................................................................

**TODAYS DATE** ...................................................................................................................................................

**Quality of sleep:** ...............................**Number of hours slept**:..................................................................

Scale: 1 = poor  Scale: 10 = deep and refreshing

**Vitality factor in morning**  (scale 1= very tired, hungover, not well, dying)

(scale: 10 = full of energy, clear headed, refreshed, generally fantastic) .......................................out of 10

**Breakfast**

Time eaten: .......................................

Food:..................................................................................................................................................

.........................................................................................................................................................

**Snack**

Time eaten: .......................................

Food:..................................................................................................................................................

.........................................................................................................................................................

**Lunch**

Time eaten: .......................................

Food:..................................................................................................................................................

.........................................................................................................................................................

.........................................................................................................................................................

**Snack**

Time eaten: .......................................

Food:..................................................................................................................................................

.........................................................................................................................................................

**Dinner**

Time eaten: .......................................

Food:..................................................................................................................................................

.........................................................................................................................................................

.........................................................................................................................................................

**Exercise**: ..........................................................................................................................................

.........................................................................................................................................................

**Quality of day out of 10**........................................................................................................................

# DAY 28

**TODAYS DATE** ................................................................................................................................................

**Quality of sleep:** ............................**Number of hours slept**: .........................................................................

Scale: 1 = poor  Scale: 10 = deep and refreshing

**Vitality factor in morning** (scale 1= very tired, hungover, not well, dying)

(scale: 10 = full of energy, clear headed, refreshed, generally fantastic) .............................................out of 10

**Breakfast**

Time eaten: .........................................

Food:............................................................................................................................................................

..........................................................................................................................................................

**Snack**

Time eaten: .........................................

Food:............................................................................................................................................................

..........................................................................................................................................................

**Lunch**

Time eaten: .........................................

Food:............................................................................................................................................................

..........................................................................................................................................................

..........................................................................................................................................................

**Snack**

Time eaten: .........................................

Food:............................................................................................................................................................

..........................................................................................................................................................

**Dinner**

Time eaten: .........................................

Food:............................................................................................................................................................

..........................................................................................................................................................

..........................................................................................................................................................

**Exercise**: ....................................................................................................................................................

..........................................................................................................................................................

**Quality of day out of 10**...........................................................................................................................

## D is for...

### Diets
Avoid them. Read The Body Talks, Heal Your Weight.

### Decaffeinated
See coffee.

### Diet foods and drinks
This refers to all foods and drinks labelled sugar free, diet, low or no fat or cholesterol free or diabetic. They are all man made, unnatural, deceptive, hide chemicals and poisonous substitute substances such as aspartame or transfatty acids and should be avoided, all of them, at all costs. I have not found one that the body says is good for it or really delivers on its promise. Someone has to say it!! The industry is worth billions because we have fallen for the marketing. These products are not researched by independent scientists: they are developed by the scientists who work for the food company which stands to make millions from a successful new food, marketed and backed up by their research. Call me cynical. Ulltimately, regular use of any of these products will lead to accelerated metabolic ageing and an unbalanced immune system.

### Digestive Detox
The cellular detox triggered by eliminating your blood type food intolerances, differs considerably from a Digestive detox. A digestive detox will range from 1 day to 3 weeks and may involve complete fasting with just water and fruit or salads, soups, juices, cabbage or a combination of these, in order to rest the digestive system while it is cleansed of trapped and toxic matter. While a good digestive detox will leave you feeling great and refreshed, the feeling is generally short lived within a week to a month of returning to normal eating. When I have asked the bodies of people who have undergone harsh digestive detoxes, particularly those which include just fruit or salads, many of them have said it was a negative experience. Although the digestive system may have been rested, it is still not long enough to bring about any deep healing of inflammation or damage to the intestines and stomach, but has been a shock to the whole body system. In the case of fruit detoxes, the body has had to deal with a huge sugar

**WEIGH AND MEASURE DAY**

weight...................... kgs/lbs
waist ............................. cm
hips ............................... cm
bust/chest ....................... cm
top of thigh..................... cm
top of arm ...................... cm
knee ............................. cm
calf................................ cm

## Weekly marks out of 10
Sleep quality .........................
Average no hours slept...........
AM vitality factor...................
Quality of week ....................
Adherence to programme.......
No of days exercised ............

NOTES AND OBSERVATIONS
.............................................
.............................................
.............................................
.............................................
.............................................
.............................................

**TODAYS DATE** ...............................................................................................................................................................

**Quality of sleep:** ..................................**Number of hours slept**: ..................................................................

Scale: 1 = poor  Scale: 10 = deep and refreshing

**Vitality factor in morning**  (scale 1= very tired, hungover, not well, dying)

(scale: 10 = full of energy, clear headed, refreshed, generally fantastic) ...........................................out of 10

**Breakfast**

Time eaten: .........................................

Food:..............................................................................................................................................................

.........................................................................................................................................................................

**Snack**

Time eaten: .........................................

Food:..............................................................................................................................................................

.........................................................................................................................................................................

**Lunch**

Time eaten: .........................................

Food:..............................................................................................................................................................

.........................................................................................................................................................................

.........................................................................................................................................................................

**Snack**

Time eaten: .........................................

Food:..............................................................................................................................................................

.........................................................................................................................................................................

**Dinner**

Time eaten: .........................................

Food:..............................................................................................................................................................

.........................................................................................................................................................................

.........................................................................................................................................................................

**Exercise**: ....................................................................................................................................................

.........................................................................................................................................................................

**Quality of day out of 10**...........................................................................................................................

input, resulting in the pancreas being worked overtime. The body generally hates any changes in routine and balance and its general wish is that detoxing occurs within the context of regular balanced meals of light proteins, vegetables and good fats. Fasting should only be done under professional supervision.

A Cellular Detox is a term I coined having watched the same pattern emerge every time that people started to avoid their intolerances. On day six of being very strict, you wake up feeling a little worse for wear, or in some cases like you have been hit by a bus! Headaches, flu symptoms, tiredness, moodiness, irritability, skin breakouts and emotional break downs are common complaints. The body will always try and return to homeostasis, or ideal health. As soon as the blood is clear of incoming intolerances, which takes 5 days, the brain sends a message to the cells telling them to release all the toxin they can. This is what you are feeling on day 6. The symptoms last for 2 or 3 days until the blood has cleared these residues through the liver and kidneys and they have been eliminated from the body. Then you will experience a couple of days of feeling better, followed by another wave of detox. These waves continue for up to 8 weeks until all the system is cleared out. Around week 6, many people report a very tired drugged feeling for about a week. This appears to be a final deep healing crisis, which takes a lot of energy and will make you very tired. Soon after this, your energy and vitality start to improve dramatically. For people clearing a particular condition, weeks 6-8 are usually a time of more severe detox symptoms of the original problem such as bad acne, tummy ache, headaches, joint pain or back ache. Then one morning they are gone. People report feeling like the mist has cleared and they can see clearly again. Their skin begins to glow from the inside, their moods improve, their energy is better than they can remember in a long time and their conditions are much improved. Stage one is over.

During stage one, the adrenal glands, those little glands on the kidneys responsible for your immune system and over 300 different functions in the body, are able to rest from the onslaught of constant food intolerances and as they recover, are able to deal more effectively with fluid retention, fat metabolism, hormonal balance, weight balance, the immune system and all its other functions. It generally takes about four months to completely heal your adrenal

**TODAYS DATE** .......................................................................................................................................................

**Quality of sleep:** .................................**Number of hours slept**: ................................................................

Scale: 1 = poor  Scale: 10 = deep and refreshing

**Vitality factor in morning**  (scale 1= very tired, hungover, not well, dying)

(scale: 10 = full of energy, clear headed, refreshed, generally fantastic) ........................................................out of 10

**Breakfast**

Time eaten: ..........................................

Food: ....................................................................................................................................................

........................................................................................................................................................

**Snack**

Time eaten: ..........................................

Food: ....................................................................................................................................................

........................................................................................................................................................

**Lunch**

Time eaten: ..........................................

Food: ....................................................................................................................................................

........................................................................................................................................................

........................................................................................................................................................

**Snack**

Time eaten: ..........................................

Food: ....................................................................................................................................................

........................................................................................................................................................

**Dinner**

Time eaten: ..........................................

Food: ....................................................................................................................................................

........................................................................................................................................................

........................................................................................................................................................

**Exercise**: ..........................................................................................................................................

........................................................................................................................................................

**Quality of day out of 10** ....................................................................................................................

glands if you have abused them for many years as most of us unwittingly have. As you move into stage 2 of your programme, you should continue to strictly avoid your food intolerances for another month if the symptoms of your ailment are still present, or you can slowly reintroduce one of your bad foods at a time and see whether your body reacts to it. If you feel no reaction, you could begin to take that food once every 4 days. This appears to be the ideal gap between each time you eat that food without it building up in your system again. If you come off your programme too quickly and return to old habits at this time, your body has not healed deeply enough to withstand the onslaught and old symptoms will quickly return. At this stage people with food intolerance conditions such as IBS, acne, headaches or such, are so relieved by the difference and their new found health, that it is not difficult for them to remain on the system and be careful about how much they eat of a certain food. Their bodies quickly tell them if they have overdone it. For others, they may become aware of mood changes or drop in concentration, a fuzziness or sleepiness that overcomes them when they cheat. It becomes a personal decision of how strict you wish to be and what quality of vitality you wish to live with versus missing out foods you love.

## NOTES AND OBSERVATIONS

.....................................
.....................................
.....................................
.....................................
.....................................
.....................................
.....................................
.....................................
.....................................
.....................................
.....................................
.....................................
.....................................
.....................................
.....................................
.....................................
.....................................
.....................................
.....................................
.....................................
.....................................
.....................................
.....................................
.....................................
.....................................
.....................................
.....................................
.....................................
.....................................
.....................................
.....................................
.....................................
.....................................

# DAY 31

**TODAYS DATE** ......................................................................................................................................................

**Quality of sleep:** ...............................**Number of hours slept**: ...........................................................................

Scale: 1 = poor  Scale: 10 = deep and refreshing

**Vitality factor in morning** (scale 1= very tired, hungover, not well, dying)

(scale: 10 = full of energy, clear headed, refreshed, generally fantastic) ..........................................................out of 10

**Breakfast**

Time eaten: ........................................

Food:..........................................................................................................................................................

.....................................................................................................................................................................

**Snack**

Time eaten: ........................................

Food:..........................................................................................................................................................

.....................................................................................................................................................................

**Lunch**

Time eaten: ........................................

Food:..........................................................................................................................................................

.....................................................................................................................................................................

.....................................................................................................................................................................

**Snack**

Time eaten: ........................................

Food:..........................................................................................................................................................

.....................................................................................................................................................................

**Dinner**

Time eaten: ........................................

Food:..........................................................................................................................................................

.....................................................................................................................................................................

.....................................................................................................................................................................

**Exercise**: ...............................................................................................................................................

.....................................................................................................................................................................

**Quality of day out of 10**..........................................................................................................................

**E is for...**

**Eggs**

Eggs are nature's wonder food and THE best food for weight loss and maintaining sugar levels. They contain a superb balance of chromium, lecithin, B vitamins, good cholesterol, fats and protein. 94% of the protein in egg is used by the body compared to only 34% of the protein in meat. Eggs do not cause high cholesterol, they actually lower it. In 1999, a study on 100,000 people in the USA looked at the relationship between egg consumption and raised cholesterol levels. There was no significant link. Eggs actually can lower cholesterol if cholesterol levels are high. Two eggs a day will convince the body it is receiving enough vital dietary cholesterol and that it can switch off the enzyme ADH reductase in the liver, whose sole job it is to manufacture extra cholesterol from incoming sugars. There is not one study that links eggs to high cholesterol and heart disease. It is an assumed relationship because eggs are high in cholesterol. In the last three years I have had 21 cases of high cholesterol, non of which were responding to normal low cholesterol diets or drugs. They returned to normal cholesterol levels within three to four months after eating two eggs a day.

Eggs can cause constipation when hard-boiled in their shells. The shell, which gives the unique toughness to the egg is released during cooking into the egg, which causes binding in the intestines. An occasional hard boiled egg is fine, but cook eggs out of their shells if you are prone to constipation. Eggs make the best breakfast. Try and buy eggs of good quality, preferably free range or corn fed with a low level of hormone or antibiotic. A fresh egg will sink when placed in water, whereas an older egg will have absorbed air through the shell and will float.

In April 1999 a study published in the Journal of American Medical Association of over 100,000 subjects, found no correlation between the daily consumption of eggs and the incidence of heart disease or strokes in men and women.

NOTES AND OBSERVATIONS

# DAY 32

**TODAYS DATE** .......................................................................................................................................................................

**Quality of sleep:** ...................................**Number of hours slept**: ...................................................................................

Scale: 1 = poor  Scale: 10 = deep and refreshing

**Vitality factor in morning**  (scale 1= very tired, hungover, not well, dying)

(scale: 10 = full of energy, clear headed, refreshed, generally fantastic) ...................................................................out of 10

**Breakfast**

Time eaten: ...........................................

Food:......................................................................................................................................................................

..............................................................................................................................................................................

**Snack**

Time eaten: ...........................................

Food:......................................................................................................................................................................

..............................................................................................................................................................................

**Lunch**

Time eaten: ...........................................

Food:......................................................................................................................................................................

..............................................................................................................................................................................

..............................................................................................................................................................................

**Snack**

Time eaten: ...........................................

Food:......................................................................................................................................................................

..............................................................................................................................................................................

**Dinner**

Time eaten: ...........................................

Food:......................................................................................................................................................................

..............................................................................................................................................................................

..............................................................................................................................................................................

**Exercise**: ..............................................................................................................................................................

..............................................................................................................................................................................

**Quality of day out of 10** .....................................................................................................................................

## Environment

Be a responsible, conscious consumer. Otherwise the tips in this book about buying the cleanest, most chemical free foods may not be an option for your children.

If you have naturally produced or organic options available to you in your supermarket or local grocer, buy whatever you can afford. Not only is it better for your health, but the more people who support organic and environmentally sustaining food, the cheaper it will become.

Household detergents and personal bath products also place a heavy burden on our water supplies. Chemically based products can take as long as 26 years to break down in the water table. Natural soaps, washing powders and cleaning products take only three days. Your local health shop will sell environmentally friendly detergents and body products.

And lastly, we cannot afford to be passive about our environment any longer and hope someone else will speak for us. The earth hinges on the point of no return, whereby our world will become so chemical, that there will be nowhere to grow anything natural or breathe clean air. Make your friends aware of better choices, recycle wherever you can and boycott brands which abuse nature in the name of profit, or are low cost brands. Everything has a price!

## Epsom Salts

Excellent for detoxing through the skin, particularly while doing a cellular detox or after exercise. Throw 3 handfuls of pure Epsom salt into the bath and soak for 15-20 minutes.

## Exercise

Strenuous exercise programmes in the first few weeks of starting a weight loss programme are counter-productive. When you are overweight, the chances are that your adrenal gland function, the gland that manages your immune system, metabolism and some 300 other functions, is very low. The long-term success of your weight loss depends on this gland functioning well. When you exercise your system above and beyond a certain level of stress, specific to each individual, the immune system can actually become weakened. Six weeks later

**TODAYS DATE** ..............................................................................................................................................................................

**Quality of sleep:** ...................................**Number of hours slept**: ..................................................................................

Scale: 1 = poor   Scale: 10 = deep and refreshing

**Vitality factor in morning**  (scale 1= very tired, hungover, not well, dying)

(scale: 10 = full of energy, clear headed, refreshed, generally fantastic) ................................................................out of 10

**Breakfast**

Time eaten: .........................................

Food:.........................................................................................................................................................................

..................................................................................................................................................................................

**Snack**

Time eaten: .........................................

Food:.........................................................................................................................................................................

..................................................................................................................................................................................

**Lunch**

Time eaten: .........................................

Food:.........................................................................................................................................................................

..................................................................................................................................................................................

..................................................................................................................................................................................

**Snack**

Time eaten: .........................................

Food:.........................................................................................................................................................................

..................................................................................................................................................................................

**Dinner**

Time eaten: .........................................

Food:.........................................................................................................................................................................

..................................................................................................................................................................................

..................................................................................................................................................................................

**Exercise**: .................................................................................................................................................................

..................................................................................................................................................................................

**Quality of day out of 10**.........................................................................................................................................

**TODAYS DATE** ...........................................................................................................................................

**Quality of sleep:** ................................**Number of hours slept**: ............................................................

Scale: 1 = poor  Scale: 10 = deep and refreshing

**Vitality factor in morning** (scale 1= very tired, hungover, not well, dying)

(scale: 10 = full of energy, clear headed, refreshed, generally fantastic) ....................................................out of 10

**Breakfast**

Time eaten: ..........................................

Food:........................................................................................................................................................

..................................................................................................................................................................

**Snack**

Time eaten: ..........................................

Food:........................................................................................................................................................

..................................................................................................................................................................

**Lunch**

Time eaten: ..........................................

Food:........................................................................................................................................................

..................................................................................................................................................................

..................................................................................................................................................................

**Snack**

Time eaten: ..........................................

Food:........................................................................................................................................................

..................................................................................................................................................................

**Dinner**

Time eaten: ..........................................

Food:........................................................................................................................................................

..................................................................................................................................................................

..................................................................................................................................................................

**Exercise**: ..............................................................................................................................................

..................................................................................................................................................................

**Quality of day out of 10**.........................................................................................................................

# DAY 35

**TODAYS DATE** ...........................................................................................................................................................

**Quality of sleep:** ............................... **Number of hours slept**: ..........................................................................

Scale: 1 = poor  Scale: 10 = deep and refreshing

**Vitality factor in morning**  (scale 1= very tired, hungover, not well, dying)

(scale: 10 = full of energy, clear headed, refreshed, generally fantastic) ..............................................................out of 10

**Breakfast**

Time eaten: ...........................................

Food: ..............................................................................................................................................................

.......................................................................................................................................................................

**Snack**

Time eaten: ...........................................

Food: ..............................................................................................................................................................

.......................................................................................................................................................................

**Lunch**

Time eaten: ...........................................

Food: ..............................................................................................................................................................

.......................................................................................................................................................................

.......................................................................................................................................................................

**Snack**

Time eaten: ...........................................

Food: ..............................................................................................................................................................

.......................................................................................................................................................................

**Dinner**

Time eaten: ...........................................

Food: ..............................................................................................................................................................

.......................................................................................................................................................................

.......................................................................................................................................................................

**Exercise**: .......................................................................................................................................................

.......................................................................................................................................................................

**Quality of day out of 10**...........................................................................................................................................

after exercising hard and following a calorie restricted diet, your body will be much sicker than it was when you started.

As the intensive exercise programme compromises your immune system, your body becomes more vulnerable to illness and you fall ill. If you have also been following a low calorie diet, you will find yourself unable to continue your programme. You will feel you need to eat more again to replace the lost nutrients, but with your now further diminished glandular system and metabolic rate, lost weight is rapidly regained together with more fat and the classic yo-yo pattern is achieved. Avoid high exercise, low calorie regimes.

## F is for...

### Fat

FAT does not make you fat. Please get over your fear of it. All fats found in nature are good for you. Saturated, monosaturated and polyunsaturated fats are all healthy, eaten in their natural state and in moderation. Our bodies have eaten them and evolved with them over thousands of years. Your diet should consist of 30% fats, coming from a variety of naturally occurring, unprocessed food such as olive oil, butter, eggs, red meat, avocado, poultry, fish, nuts and seeds.

The body needs the full range of fats found in natural foods for many vital functions in the body. The brain comprises 60% fat. Dietary fats, as opposed to body fat already stored in fat cells, play a vital role in many different functions in the body, including metabolism, the absorption of protein and carbohydrates, the breakdown of nutrients, the brain processes and the manufacture of hormones. A deficiency of fat may result in:

● Mood disorders and depression
● Constipation
● Infertility
● Insomnia
● Sugar and carbohydrate cravings
● Brittle nails, dry skin and thin, limp hair

It takes a certain amount of fat in your meal to feel satisfied and a low fat diet

**WEIGH AND MEASURE DAY**

weight...................... kgs/lbs
waist ............................. cm
hips ............................... cm
bust/chest ....................... cm
top of thigh ..................... cm
top of arm ...................... cm
knee .............................. cm
calf................................ cm

## Weekly marks out of 10
Sleep quality ........................
Average no hours slept...........
AM vitality factor...................
Quality of week ....................
Adherence to programme.......
No of days exercised ...........

NOTES AND OBSERVATIONS
...........................................
...........................................
...........................................
...........................................
...........................................
...........................................

# DAY 36

**TODAYS DATE** ...............................................................................................................................................................

**Quality of sleep:** .................................**Number of hours slept**: ..............................................................................
Scale: 1 = poor  Scale: 10 = deep and refreshing

**Vitality factor in morning**  (scale 1= very tired, hungover, not well, dying)
(scale: 10 = full of energy, clear headed, refreshed, generally fantastic) ..................................................................out of 10

**Breakfast**
Time eaten: ...........................................
Food:...........................................................................................................................................................................
............................................................................................................................................................................

**Snack**
Time eaten: ...........................................
Food:...........................................................................................................................................................................
............................................................................................................................................................................

**Lunch**
Time eaten: ...........................................
Food:...........................................................................................................................................................................
............................................................................................................................................................................
............................................................................................................................................................................

**Snack**
Time eaten: ...........................................
Food:...........................................................................................................................................................................
............................................................................................................................................................................

**Dinner**
Time eaten: ...........................................
Food:...........................................................................................................................................................................
............................................................................................................................................................................
............................................................................................................................................................................

**Exercise**: ................................................................................................................................................................
............................................................................................................................................................................

**Quality of day out of 10**...................................................................................................................................................

will eventually lead you to craving more carbohydrate because you have a hard time feeling like you have eaten enough. Increase your intake of good natural fats and you will find your cravings lessen. Known to be particularly important to the body and excellent at preventing heart disease are the Omega 3 and Omega 6 fatty acids. Foods containing vital Omega 3 fatty acids include fish, olive oil, nuts, seeds and avocado. Omega 6 is obtained from leafy greens, pulses and whole unrefined grains such as rye, oats and barley. Both these fatty vitamins must be consumed regularly in our food, though we are more commonly deficient in the Omego 3 fats. Omega 3 will also boost your metabolic rate and act as a diuretic.

When you eat fats, they do not turn into fat because they do not stimulate insulin release, like sugars and carbohydrates do, Insulin is the catalyst needed to convert dietary fat into body fat. Fat cannot be stored without the presence of insulin because insulin is necessary to open the doors to the fat cells and like a bossy prison warden, shove it into the fat cells and locks it in. If there is no insulin circulating in the blood stream, fats cannot be stored.

**Fish**

Fish is an excellent form of digestible high quality protein and should be eaten often. It contains high levels of essential fatty acids and low levels of saturated fats. Most 'B' blood types I have tested have been intolerant to Red Snapper and Mullet but generally all the blood types love all the different fish. An intolerance to shellfish is quite common amongst the 'O' and 'B' bloodtypes, whose ascendants evolved inland and had very little or no access to the sea. The occasional 'O' or 'B' blood type I have tested that could tolerate shellfish, often knew that their ancestors were coastal dwellers. Most 'A' and 'AB' blood types love and thrive on shellfish. If you are allergic to shellfish, you will have found out the hard way already! An allergy to one or more shellfish seems to be fairly well distributed throughout all four blood types.

Some people, particularly descendants of the Scandinavians, the North American Coastal people and the Celtic Irish, Scottish or Welsh require a very special need for essential fats, namely Omega 3, due to their ancestors reliance on fish for as long as 20,000 years. If you have inherited a gene from this stock, your genetic code adapted itself to a fish based diet and you may still require

# DAY 37

**TODAYS DATE** .......................................................................................................................................................

**Quality of sleep:** .............................**Number of hours slept**: ..............................................................................
Scale: 1 = poor  Scale: 10 = deep and refreshing

**Vitality factor in morning** (scale 1= very tired, hungover, not well, dying)

(scale: 10 = full of energy, clear headed, refreshed, generally fantastic) .............................................................out of 10

## Breakfast

Time eaten: ......................................

Food:........................................................................................................................................................................

...............................................................................................................................................................................

## Snack

Time eaten: ......................................

Food:........................................................................................................................................................................

...............................................................................................................................................................................

## Lunch

Time eaten: ......................................

Food:........................................................................................................................................................................

...............................................................................................................................................................................

...............................................................................................................................................................................

## Snack

Time eaten: ......................................

Food:........................................................................................................................................................................

...............................................................................................................................................................................

## Dinner

Time eaten: ......................................

Food:........................................................................................................................................................................

...............................................................................................................................................................................

...............................................................................................................................................................................

**Exercise**: ...............................................................................................................................................................

...............................................................................................................................................................................

**Quality of day out of 10**.....................................................................................................................................

lots of fish fat. Fish fats provide a very high source of the brain activating food known as DHA. People with this ancestry may not yet be able to make this out of other non fish sources such as flax seeds, walnuts or olive oil. Without enough of this fish based Omega 3 in their diet, descendents of Scandinavians, Celts or Coastal native Americans are prone to depression due to a deficiency of DHA and may find themselves craving for alcohol. If you are prone to craving alcohol or using it to numb depression, try taking a fish oil supplement such as cod liver or salmon oil and eat at least 4 portions of fatty fish such as salmon, mackerel, tuna or sardines a week.

## Fruit

Fruit is highly overrated as a health food! Fruit is pure sugar. If it is picked fresh and consumed within a few days, it does indeed contain many wonderful vitamins, but these vitamins are quickly oxidized once the fruit is picked. Historically, fruit appeared in abundance at harvest time, when people were working very hard, out in the fields and needed the quick extra supply of natural sugar in the sun. Fruit was then picked, preserved and eeked out over long winter months, eaten in very limited amounts. Today, we eat it like it is candy, and indeed it is just that. Most of the fruit we buy from our supermarkets today were picked unripe before they had developed their full vitamin content, are then shipped across the world and hit the shelves as much as four weeks later. One medium green apple, contains around three teaspoons of white sugar equivalent in fructose. A banana contains six!! It is indeed natures' candy! When you eat fruit for breakfast you are giving your body a sugar overload, which inevitably results in a rapid hike in blood sugar level, followed shortly by a dramatic drop as the insulin kicks in, leaving you with that hunger pang by mid morning.

Treat fruit with respect, never eat it on its own, it digests so quickly on an empty stomach that the sugar enters the liver too fast for it to be used by the muscles and inevitably some must be stored as body fat. By combining fruit with some protein, or eating it after a balanced meal, you will slow down the digestion of the sugars and ensure that you avoid a sugar rush. Most bodies recommend you limit your daily fruit intake to just two portions a day. Rely on vegetables for your nutrients and fibre. There is also a myth that fruit should be eaten before a meal and not afterwards. Fruit contains digestive enzymes that will help the efficient

# DAY 38

**TODAYS DATE** ..................................................................................................................................................

**Quality of sleep:** .................................**Number of hours slept**: ...............................................................

Scale: 1 = poor  Scale: 10 = deep and refreshing

**Vitality factor in morning**  (scale 1= very tired, hungover, not well, dying)

(scale: 10 = full of energy, clear headed, refreshed, generally fantastic) .............................................................out of 10

**Breakfast**

Time eaten: ...........................................

Food:.....................................................................................................................................................

..............................................................................................................................................................

**Snack**

Time eaten: ...........................................

Food:.....................................................................................................................................................

..............................................................................................................................................................

**Lunch**

Time eaten: ...........................................

Food:.....................................................................................................................................................

..............................................................................................................................................................

..............................................................................................................................................................

**Snack**

Time eaten: ...........................................

Food:.....................................................................................................................................................

..............................................................................................................................................................

**Dinner**

Time eaten: ...........................................

Food:.....................................................................................................................................................

..............................................................................................................................................................

..............................................................................................................................................................

**Exercise**: ..............................................................................................................................................

..............................................................................................................................................................

**Quality of day out of 10**.......................................................................................................................

digestion of your meal if eaten after the main course. Eaten before a meal, ensures the fruit will have already considerably digested and the enzymes lost, before the protein in your meal can really slow it down. So often people are surprised that they do not lose weight when they think they are being healthy by eating lots of fruit and little else. Now you know why it doesn't work!

**Frying**

Frying in ANY oil including olive oil causes short-term memory loss according to the body as heated oils change their molecular structure and become very toxic. Heating to high temperatures such as those reached during frying, damages fat, which cannot be recognised by the body and broken down and properly digested and eliminated. These then become cellular toxic waste, which directly affects the brain and damages cells by clogging them up. The accumulated debris causes accelerated ageing and contributes to furring up of arteries. Any unnatural man made fat, such as sunflower and corn oils, margarines and other low fat spreads which are also damaged fats do the same thing. The body has recommended we fry in butter or ghee, not a lot and not often, but as these are saturated fats, they remain stable in a safe digestible form at high temperatures.

...................................
...................................
...................................
...................................
...................................
...................................
...................................
...................................
...................................
...................................
...................................
...................................
...................................
...................................
...................................
...................................
...................................
...................................
...................................
...................................
...................................
...................................
...................................
...................................
...................................
...................................
...................................
...................................
...................................
...................................
...................................
...................................
...................................
...................................

# DAY 39

**TODODAYS DATE** ....................................................................................................................................

**Quality of sleep:** .................................**Number of hours slept**: ........................................................

Scale: 1 = poor  Scale: 10 = deep and refreshing

**Vitality factor in morning**  (scale 1= very tired, hungover, not well, dying)

(scale: 10 = full of energy, clear headed, refreshed, generally fantastic) ...........................................out of 10

**Breakfast**

Time eaten: ...........................................

Food:..................................................................................................................................................

...........................................................................................................................................................

**Snack**

Time eaten: ...........................................

Food:..................................................................................................................................................

...........................................................................................................................................................

**Lunch**

Time eaten: ...........................................

Food:..................................................................................................................................................

...........................................................................................................................................................

...........................................................................................................................................................

**Snack**

Time eaten: ...........................................

Food:..................................................................................................................................................

...........................................................................................................................................................

**Dinner**

Time eaten: ...........................................

Food:..................................................................................................................................................

...........................................................................................................................................................

...........................................................................................................................................................

**Exercise**: .........................................................................................................................................

...........................................................................................................................................................

**Quality of day out of 10** ...................................................................................................................

## G is for...

### Genetically Engineered Foods

Genetically engineered foods contain genes from other plants and animals, introduced to give them certain qualities such as a higher yield, a certain flavour or resistance to certain pests. The problem is there have been no long-term human safety tests done on the consumption of these foods, nor do we really know the impact that they may have on our natural world.

Initial evidence is very worrying and is showing strong warning signs of its massive impact on the future of our environment and our health. Genetic pollution from pollen drift is spreading widely outside the test growth areas, costing millions in lost export sales. In Iowa, in North America, corn farmers planted 1% of their crop in GE "Starlink" seed, not approved for human consumption. Within 12 months, 50% of the entire Iowa corn crop tested positive for traces of the Starlink gene, according to David Gould of Farm Verified Organic. Super weeds, resistant to known herbicides, are appearing in areas planted with GM seeds containing a herbicide resistant gene.

The worrying increase of asthma in Britain has exactly mirrored the increase in imports of genetically engineered soy being imported from America.

For those of us intolerant to certain natural foods, the implications of GM foods are terrifying. You will not know if you are eating a food which contains an element of something that makes you ill. If it takes the human body so many years (around 10-20 generations) to become tolerant to a new natural food, what will be the damage to our health on a global level with the introduction of GM foods? There is also no room for experimentation here. Once these pollens are released, we can never go back.

### Gluten

Gluten is a protein found in most grains such as wheat, oats, barley and rye. Corn, rice and millet do not contain gluten. Gluten is a protein that in some people attacks the lining of the stomach and causes inflammation and even ulceration of the delicate digestive tract. In some cases the gluten protein interferes directly with the brain or delicate membranes throughout the body, such

**TODAYS DATE** ................................................................................................................................................................................

**Quality of sleep:** ..............................**Number of hours slept**: .................................................................................................

Scale: 1 = poor  Scale: 10 = deep and refreshing

**Vitality factor in morning**  (scale 1= very tired, hungover, not well, dying)

(scale: 10 = full of energy, clear headed, refreshed, generally fantastic) ................................................................out of 10

**Breakfast**

Time eaten: ...........................................

Food:...............................................................................................................................................................................

........................................................................................................................................................................................

**Snack**

Time eaten: ...........................................

Food:...............................................................................................................................................................................

........................................................................................................................................................................................

**Lunch**

Time eaten: ...........................................

Food:...............................................................................................................................................................................

........................................................................................................................................................................................

........................................................................................................................................................................................

**Snack**

Time eaten: ...........................................

Food:...............................................................................................................................................................................

........................................................................................................................................................................................

**Dinner**

Time eaten: ...........................................

Food:...............................................................................................................................................................................

........................................................................................................................................................................................

........................................................................................................................................................................................

**Exercise**: .......................................................................................................................................................................

........................................................................................................................................................................................

**Quality of day out of 10**.............................................................................................................................................

**TODAYS DATE** .................................................................................................................

**Quality of sleep:** .............................................**Number of hours slept**: ......................................

Scale: 1 = poor  Scale: 10 = deep and refreshing

**Vitality factor in morning** (scale 1= very tired, hungover, not well, dying)

(scale: 10 = full of energy, clear headed, refreshed, generally fantastic) ...........................................out of 10

**Breakfast**

Time eaten: ...........................................

Food:................................................................................................................................

........................................................................................................................................

**Snack**

Time eaten: ...........................................

Food:................................................................................................................................

........................................................................................................................................

**Lunch**

Time eaten: ...........................................

Food:................................................................................................................................

........................................................................................................................................

........................................................................................................................................

**Snack**

Time eaten: ...........................................

Food:................................................................................................................................

........................................................................................................................................

**Dinner**

Time eaten: ...........................................

Food:................................................................................................................................

........................................................................................................................................

........................................................................................................................................

**Exercise**: ........................................................................................................................

........................................................................................................................................

**Quality of day out of 10**.................................................................................................

74

# DAY 42

**TODODAYS DATE** ...........................................................................................................................................................

**Quality of sleep:** ...........................**Number of hours slept**: ..............................................................................
Scale: 1 = poor  Scale: 10 = deep and refreshing

**Vitality factor in morning** (scale 1= very tired, hungover, not well, dying)
(scale: 10 = full of energy, clear headed, refreshed, generally fantastic) ................................................................out of 10

**Breakfast**
Time eaten: ...........................................
Food:...........................................................................................................................................................
...........................................................................................................................................................

**Snack**
Time eaten: ...........................................
Food:...........................................................................................................................................................
...........................................................................................................................................................

**Lunch**
Time eaten: ...........................................
Food:...........................................................................................................................................................
...........................................................................................................................................................
...........................................................................................................................................................

**Snack**
Time eaten: ...........................................
Food:...........................................................................................................................................................
...........................................................................................................................................................

**Dinner**
Time eaten: ...........................................
Food:...........................................................................................................................................................
...........................................................................................................................................................
...........................................................................................................................................................

**Exercise**: ...................................................................................................................................................
...........................................................................................................................................................
**Quality of day out of 10** ...............................................................................................................................

as in the joints or sinuses. A true gluten allergy is quite rare, occurring in only 1 in 250 people I test. This condition is known medically as Coeliac disease and can be very serious. It is closely associated with both diabetes and colon cancer. If you are wheat intolerant it does not mean you are gluten intolerant. Most people are intolerant to the modifications in the make up of modern day wheat, not to the gluten. Gluten free breads and biscuits are automatically wheat free and can be used in a wheat free diet, but are not necessary. People with gluten allergies can only eat gluten free starches, such as corn, rice, potato, quinoa, millet, maize and kamut.

## Saliva, Blood, Skin Prick, or Biopsy for Severe Gluten Intolerances (Coeliac Disease)

If you suspect you have a gluten allergy, the gold standard for hormone testing according to the World Health Organisation is a saliva test, which seems to identify it reliably from mild to severe. The blood test only seems to identify the most severe coeliac cases. Specialised skin-prick testing is another reliable allergy test, but the most accurate way of diagnosing true coeliac disease is by biopsy of the small intestine. The body will tell me the level of intolerance or allergy to gluten by a percentage value, but when I suspect a gluten allergy I always ask people to get a medical test to confirm this.

Gluten intolerance is a much milder form of this reaction, which many people may suffer. Grains are generally difficult to digest and I do not advise anyone to eat too many of them. The phytic acid found in grains is also known to block the absorption of calcium. Grains are also a starch form of carbohydrate and contain high amounts of concentrated sugars. Common gluten intolerance symptoms, usually only felt with the higher levels of gluten found in modern day wheat, include bloating, gas, low energy, fluid retention, cellulite and even sleepiness.

Modern day wheat is the result of 150 years of selective breeding and hybridisation and is approximately three times higher in gluten than original spelt wheat. Rye, barley and oats are still fairly close to their original natural form and have been, in their current form, in the human diet for hundreds of years. It is not known exactly how the changes from original spelt into new modern wheat have affected us, but there is no doubt that an increasing number of people today are

**WEIGH AND MEASURE DAY**

weight...................... kgs/lbs
waist ............................. cm
hips ............................... cm
bust/chest ...................... cm
top of thigh..................... cm
top of arm ...................... cm
knee .............................. cm
calf................................ cm

### Weekly marks out of 10

Sleep quality ........................
Average no hours slept...........
AM vitality factor ...................
Quality of week ....................
Adherence to programme.......
No of days exercised ............

### NOTES AND OBSERVATIONS

.................................................
.................................................
.................................................
.................................................
.................................................
.................................................

**TODAYS DATE** ................................................................................................................................................

**Quality of sleep:** ...........................**Number of hours slept**: ...............................................................

Scale: 1 = poor  Scale: 10 = deep and refreshing

**Vitality factor in morning**  (scale 1= very tired, hungover, not well, dying)

(scale: 10 = full of energy, clear headed, refreshed, generally fantastic) ............................................out of 10

**Breakfast**

Time eaten: .........................................

Food:.....................................................................................................................................................

.............................................................................................................................................................

**Snack**

Time eaten: .........................................

Food:.....................................................................................................................................................

.............................................................................................................................................................

**Lunch**

Time eaten: .........................................

Food:.....................................................................................................................................................

.............................................................................................................................................................

.............................................................................................................................................................

**Snack**

Time eaten: .........................................

Food:.....................................................................................................................................................

.............................................................................................................................................................

**Dinner**

Time eaten: .........................................

Food:.....................................................................................................................................................

.............................................................................................................................................................

.............................................................................................................................................................

**Exercise**: ..........................................................................................................................................

.............................................................................................................................................................

**Quality of day out of 10**................................................................................................................

suffering adverse effects in some way from it. 94% of the 2000 people I have tested to date were intolerant to modern wheat, not gluten, and were able to eat original spelt wheat, rye, barley and oats.

## Goats milk

Goat's milk is lactose free and ideal for those unable to take dairy foods. It is nutritious and balanced and is a much better substitute for dairy than soya milk, particularly in infants. It is now readily available in most countries in supermarkets and can be used for drinking and cooking. It is stronger tasting than cow's milk and not to everyone's taste.

## Grapes

Both red and white grapes contain high amounts of fructose and when eaten in excess are very fattening. 15 small or 7 large grapes are the equivalent of three teaspoons of white sugar. Grapes have yeast on their skins that turns grape juice into wine and should be avoided if you suspect you are yeast intolerant. If you are, you will be intolerant to wine as well. Red grapes contain high levels of oxalic acid which may cause inflammation in the joints.

# DAY 44

**TODAYS DATE** ....................................................................................................................................................................

**Quality of sleep:** ...................................**Number of hours slept**: ...........................................................................

Scale: 1 = poor  Scale: 10 = deep and refreshing

**Vitality factor in morning**  (scale 1= very tired, hungover, not well, dying)

(scale: 10 = full of energy, clear headed, refreshed, generally fantastic) ...................................................out of 10

**Breakfast**

Time eaten: ...........................................

Food:............................................................................................................................................................

....................................................................................................................................................................

**Snack**

Time eaten: ...........................................

Food:............................................................................................................................................................

....................................................................................................................................................................

**Lunch**

Time eaten: ...........................................

Food:............................................................................................................................................................

....................................................................................................................................................................

....................................................................................................................................................................

**Snack**

Time eaten: ...........................................

Food:............................................................................................................................................................

....................................................................................................................................................................

**Dinner**

Time eaten: ...........................................

Food:............................................................................................................................................................

....................................................................................................................................................................

....................................................................................................................................................................

**Exercise**: ..................................................................................................................................................

....................................................................................................................................................................

**Quality of day out of 10**..........................................................................................................................

## H is for...

### Haemorrhoids

A very common ailment for many people. The two cures that the body has repeatedly recommended and which have worked time after time is to cut out wheat from the diet and take an Omega 3 supplement in the form of cod liver oil or flax seed oil. If you are an 'A' or 'AB' blood type, take the fish oil option. 'O' and 'B' types do better with the flax seed. Take 2 or 3 x 1000mg capsules daily.

### Herbs

Herbs are nature's greatest healing gift. They are also far more effective in providing vitamins and nutrients than pure supplements as their natural form makes them more absorbable and available to the body.

I have asked every one of my clients what supplements their body needs. Most of my clients come to me with problems, such as their immune systems are low and they need nutritional support. The body will 'ask' for certain vitamins, minerals and supplements in high doses for short periods of time, of only 2 to 3 months. These act like rocket fuel to push the body functions back into orbit, but once the body is functioning more efficiently again, the diet is corrected and the underlying pathogens have been eliminated, it refuses any further supplements, as long as their diet is balanced and sufficient. In any situation, the body prefers regular breaks from taking any supplement regularly. It then prefers to take nutrients from herbs. Herbs are a food in their natural state and contain balanced elements that are highly beneficial to health.

## Some Good Herbs for everyday health

| | |
|---|---|
| Alfalfa | Complete natural multivitamin. Take 1200mg daily |
| Hawthorn Berry | Excellent for strengthening the heart and circulation Take 500-1000mg daily for three to six months |
| Butchers Broom | Effective for strengthening the capillary walls and improving circulation. Can help reduce red veins and varicose veins. Take 500-1000mg daily |

# DAY 45

**TODAYS DATE** ..............................................................................................................................................

**Quality of sleep:** ...............................**Number of hours slept**: ..................................................................
Scale: 1 = poor  Scale: 10 = deep and refreshing

**Vitality factor in morning**  (scale 1= very tired, hungover, not well, dying)
(scale: 10 = full of energy, clear headed, refreshed, generally fantastic) ..........................................................out of 10

**Breakfast**

Time eaten: ...............................................

Food:..........................................................................................................................................................

..................................................................................................................................................................

**Snack**

Time eaten: ...............................................

Food:..........................................................................................................................................................

..................................................................................................................................................................

**Lunch**

Time eaten: ...............................................

Food:..........................................................................................................................................................

..................................................................................................................................................................

..................................................................................................................................................................

**Snack**

Time eaten: ...............................................

Food:..........................................................................................................................................................

..................................................................................................................................................................

**Dinner**

Time eaten: ...............................................

Food:..........................................................................................................................................................

..................................................................................................................................................................

..................................................................................................................................................................

**Exercise**: ..................................................................................................................................................

..................................................................................................................................................................

**Quality of day out of 10**...........................................................................................................................

| | | NOTES AND OBSERVATIONS |
|---|---|---|
| Goldenseal | Excellent tonic, detoxifier and anti-ageing herb. Take 500mg two to three times a week | |
| Milk Thistle | Liver detoxifier. Take 300mg for one month | |
| Wild Yam | Replaces low progesterone during menopause. Natural hormone replacement option. Use 1500mg daily during menopause. Do not use with chemical HRT. | |

(Available in most health shops)

## Herbal Teas

If you are an 'O', 'B' or 'AB' blood type, coffee and black tea, such as breakfast, Earl Grey, Darjeeling for example, will not be good for you, whether or not you are intolerant to caffeine. Therefore decaffeinated tea or coffee is not better for you. There are however good substitutes for both which also have health benefits that coffee and black tea do not have. The following teas are good for....

| Tea | Good for... |
|---|---|
| Aniseed | Boosting the immune system |
| Chamomile | Relieving upset stomachs, colds and fevers in children. A sleep inducer and mild sedative |
| Dandelion | Tastes more like coffee. Excellent for the absorption of iron |
| Ginger | Increases stomach acid secretion, very good digestive, especially for the 'A' and 'AB' blood types |
| Ginseng | A positive effect on the nervous system, particularly for the 'B' blood type. |
| Goldenseal | Indigestion and liver disorders. A natural laxative and diuretic. A weak tea can help to relieve nausea during pregnancy |
| Fennel and Nettle | Cleansing the kidneys and detoxifying the blood |
| Peppermint | Tummy ache and digestive bloating and gas. Stimulates digestive secretions |
| Rooibos or Redbush | A South African tea which tastes and brews similar to black tea. Has excellent antioxidant and general health tonic properties. Caffeine free and very low in tannin |
| Rose Hips | A good kidney and bladder tonic. Very high in vitamin C and helpful in preventing colds |
| Sarsaparilla | Boosting the immune system and can kill some viruses. Excellent blood purifier and detoxification tea. |
| Thyme (Zatar) | A good immune booster and tonic for the throat and voice. |
| Yerba mate | The Body tells me this is excellent for reducing fluid retention in response to eating foods you are intolerant to. Two cups of tea must be taken daily for 3-4 months for full effect. Currently on trial by yours truly who suffers badly with this. Initial response is encourageing! |

# DAY 46

**TODAYS DATE** ...........................................................................................................................................

**Quality of sleep:** ..............................**Number of hours slept**: ...........................................................
Scale: 1 = poor  Scale: 10 = deep and refreshing

**Vitality factor in morning** (scale 1= very tired, hungover, not well, dying)
(scale: 10 = full of energy, clear headed, refreshed, generally fantastic) ..............................................out of 10

**Breakfast**

Time eaten: ...........................................

Food:.................................................................................................................................................
.........................................................................................................................................................

**Snack**

Time eaten: ...........................................

Food:.................................................................................................................................................
.........................................................................................................................................................

**Lunch**

Time eaten: ...........................................

Food:.................................................................................................................................................
.........................................................................................................................................................
.........................................................................................................................................................

**Snack**

Time eaten: ...........................................

Food:.................................................................................................................................................
.........................................................................................................................................................

**Dinner**

Time eaten: ...........................................

Food:.................................................................................................................................................
.........................................................................................................................................................
.........................................................................................................................................................

**Exercise**: ........................................................................................................................................
.........................................................................................................................................................

**Quality of day out of 10**...............................................................................................................................

## Hernia

A hiatus hernia occurs when a tear develops in the diaphragm under the ribs, usually from trauma and an excess of acidic rich foods. A severe harsh cough can cause a tear in rare cases. The tear allows the lining of the stomach to push through the diaphragm where any quick movement results in it being pinched, causing considerable sharp pain and discomfort. The pinching sets up inflammation in the stomach wall which is then very reactive to acidic foods, such as onions, oranges, alcohol, hot spices, cooked tomatoes and fried food, causing further pain and discomfort. The discomfort can be managed by avoiding the foods which aggravate the inflammation, but the hernia will need surgery to be repaired properly.

## High density Cholesterol

High-density cholesterol or HDL's, (High Density Lipoproteins) are considered good because they take cholesterol back to the liver and therefore are thought to protect against heart disease by keeping your arteries clean. High oestrogen levels maintain good HDL levels. A diet low in fat and high in carbohydrates will deplete oestrogen levels in men and women and it is vital to consume enough good fats in your diet such as olive oil, butter, avocado, fish and nuts. The higher the level of HDL cholesterol in your body, the better.

## Honey

Honey is a natural sugar and is a better sweetener than either sugar or chemical substitutes. It is still however a form of sugar and will trigger insulin in the blood. Use sparingly to sweeten plain yoghurt and herbal teas. A teaspoon of honey a day, if grown in your local area, may help combat hay fever during the summer. Because the bees have gathered the pollen from the grasses and plants that are causing your symptoms, the honey acts as a vaccine against them, often reducing your reaction. It will need to be taken for at least three months for the effect to be felt.

DAY 47

**TODAYS DATE** ........................................................................................................................................................

**Quality of sleep:** ............................**Number of hours slept**: ...........................................................................

Scale: 1 = poor  Scale: 10 = deep and refreshing

**Vitality factor in morning** (scale 1= very tired, hungover, not well, dying)

(scale: 10 = full of energy, clear headed, refreshed, generally fantastic) ...............................................................out of 10

**Breakfast**

Time eaten: ............................................

Food:....................................................................................................................................................

........................................................................................................................................................

**Snack**

Time eaten: ............................................

Food:....................................................................................................................................................

........................................................................................................................................................

**Lunch**

Time eaten: ............................................

Food:....................................................................................................................................................

........................................................................................................................................................

........................................................................................................................................................

**Snack**

Time eaten: ............................................

Food:....................................................................................................................................................

........................................................................................................................................................

**Dinner**

Time eaten: ............................................

Food:....................................................................................................................................................

........................................................................................................................................................

........................................................................................................................................................

**Exercise**: ..............................................................................................................................................

........................................................................................................................................................

**Quality of day out of 10**..........................................................................................................................

**TODAYS DATE** .......................................................................................................................................................................................

**Quality of sleep:** ...................................**Number of hours slept**: ...............................................................................................

Scale: 1 = poor  Scale: 10 = deep and refreshing

**Vitality factor in morning** (scale 1= very tired, hungover, not well, dying)

(scale: 10 = full of energy, clear headed, refreshed, generally fantastic) ........................................................out of 10

**Breakfast**

Time eaten: ...........................................

Food:.................................................................................................................................................................................

............................................................................................................................................................................................

**Snack**

Time eaten: ...........................................

Food:.................................................................................................................................................................................

............................................................................................................................................................................................

**Lunch**

Time eaten: ...........................................

Food:.................................................................................................................................................................................

............................................................................................................................................................................................

............................................................................................................................................................................................

**Snack**

Time eaten: ...........................................

Food:.................................................................................................................................................................................

............................................................................................................................................................................................

**Dinner**

Time eaten: ...........................................

Food:.................................................................................................................................................................................

............................................................................................................................................................................................

............................................................................................................................................................................................

**Exercise**: ......................................................................................................................................................................

............................................................................................................................................................................................

**Quality of day out of 10**...............................................................................................................................................

# DAY 49

**TODAYS DATE** ...........................................................................................................................................................

**Quality of sleep:** ...................................**Number of hours slept**: ................................................................................

Scale: 1 = poor  Scale: 10 = deep and refreshing

**Vitality factor in morning** (scale 1= very tired, hungover, not well, dying)

(scale: 10 = full of energy, clear headed, refreshed, generally fantastic) ...........................................................out of 10

**Breakfast**

Time eaten: ...........................................

Food:...........................................................................................................................................................................

.....................................................................................................................................................................................

**Snack**

Time eaten: ...........................................

Food:...........................................................................................................................................................................

.....................................................................................................................................................................................

**Lunch**

Time eaten: ...........................................

Food:...........................................................................................................................................................................

.....................................................................................................................................................................................

.....................................................................................................................................................................................

**Snack**

Time eaten: ...........................................

Food:...........................................................................................................................................................................

.....................................................................................................................................................................................

**Dinner**

Time eaten: ...........................................

Food:...........................................................................................................................................................................

.....................................................................................................................................................................................

.....................................................................................................................................................................................

**Exercise**: .................................................................................................................................................................

.....................................................................................................................................................................................

**Quality of day out of 10** ..........................................................................................................................................

## I is for...

### Ice cream

If you are lactose intolerant, many people can still tolerate real ice cream, made with cream, as the cream is the fat of the milk and contains no lactose. Go for the really good makes such as Ben and Jerry's, Baskin Robbins and Häagen Dazs, which do not contain any milk, but are made with pure cream. Beware the sugar in ice cream and eat it after a meal to slow down the digestion of the sugar. Good ice-cream substitutes for those who are very sensitive to lactose include frozen yoghurts (the lactose in yoghurt is broken down by the live bacteria), sorbets and the occasional soy ice cream which, if eaten rarely, will not have any detrimental effects on your body.

### Immune system

Your Immune System is your most precious possession. Without a strong immune system protecting you from a continual onslaught of viruses, bacteria, parasites, toxins and diseases, you would be constantly ill. Long-term, a weakened immune system leaves you more vulnerable to cancer. Do not ignore this warning! As more and more super bugs and super viruses mutate in response to the overuse of antibiotics, a strong immune system is our only means of defence. These super bugs will have you in bed for months. In 2002 a bronchitis like super bug hit many parts of the world. Many people were ill for up to 4 months, as there were no antibiotics that could fight it. Just as they felt they were getting better, they got worse again. It took those with a low immune system up to 6 months to regain their health. The SARS virus is another prime example. It killed the poor, the malnourished and the elderly mainly, people whose immune systems were already compromised.

**To protect your immune system follow these guidelines for general good health.**

● Get enough sleep; you need at least 6 hours of deep sleep a night. Too much sleep is also detrimental to the immune system and if you find you consistently sleep only 5 hours before waking, this may be all you need. Do not sleep more than 8 to 9 hours a night in general. Sleep taken before midnight is more beneficial than after midnight due to the higher levels of energy from the

**WEIGH AND MEASURE DAY**

weight...................... kgs/lbs
waist ............................. cm
hips ................................ cm
bust/chest ....................... cm
top of thigh..................... cm
top of arm ...................... cm
knee ............................... cm
calf................................. cm

**Weekly marks out of 10**

Sleep quality ........................
Average no hours slept...........
AM vitality factor...................
Quality of week ....................
Adherence to programme.......
No of days exercised ............

NOTES AND OBSERVATIONS
......................................
......................................
......................................
......................................
......................................
......................................

**TODAYS DATE** .................................................................................................................................................................................

**Quality of sleep:** ............................**Number of hours slept**: ....................................................................................
Scale: 1 = poor  Scale: 10 = deep and refreshing

**Vitality factor in morning** (scale 1= very tired, hungover, not well, dying)

(scale: 10 = full of energy, clear headed, refreshed, generally fantastic) ...................................................................out of 10

**Breakfast**

Time eaten: .........................................

Food:.............................................................................................................................................................................

.......................................................................................................................................................................

**Snack**

Time eaten: .........................................

Food:.............................................................................................................................................................................

.......................................................................................................................................................................

**Lunch**

Time eaten: .........................................

Food:.............................................................................................................................................................................

.......................................................................................................................................................................

.......................................................................................................................................................................

**Snack**

Time eaten: .........................................

Food:.............................................................................................................................................................................

.......................................................................................................................................................................

**Dinner**

Time eaten: .........................................

Food:.............................................................................................................................................................................

.......................................................................................................................................................................

.......................................................................................................................................................................

**Exercise**:.....................................................................................................................................................................

.......................................................................................................................................................................

**Quality of day out of 10**.......................................................................................................................................................

sun left in the atmosphere, which gradually disperses as the night draws on.

- Manage your stress levels by becoming aware of your patterns and triggers. Seek help to learn new ways of seeing things differently or managing your time

- Avoid your food intolerances. The body cannot heal the immune system if it is constantly being burdened by foods which do not suit your individual blood type

- Minimise your alcohol consumption. The human body was never designed to drink alcohol on a regular basis

- Eat healthy foods low in chemicals and high in nutrients. Avoid junk foods and processed foods

- Don't smoke or take unnecessary pharmaceutical drugs

- Cut down on your sugar intake

- Take moderate regular exercise

- Get outside for a hour every day if you work in an office

## NOTES AND OBSERVATIONS

.....................................
.....................................
.....................................
.....................................
.....................................
.....................................
.....................................
.....................................
.....................................
.....................................
.....................................
.....................................
.....................................
.....................................
.....................................
.....................................
.....................................
.....................................
.....................................
.....................................
.....................................
.....................................
.....................................
.....................................
.....................................
.....................................
.....................................
.....................................
.....................................
.....................................
.....................................
.....................................

# DAY 51

**TODAYS DATE** ........................................................................................................................................

**Quality of sleep:** ...................................**Number of hours slept**: ...........................................................
Scale: 1 = poor  Scale: 10 = deep and refreshing

**Vitality factor in morning** (scale 1= very tired, hungover, not well, dying)
(scale: 10 = full of energy, clear headed, refreshed, generally fantastic) .........................................out of 10

**Breakfast**

Time eaten: ........................................

Food:...................................................................................................................................................
.............................................................................................................................................................

**Snack**

Time eaten: ........................................

Food:...................................................................................................................................................
.............................................................................................................................................................

**Lunch**

Time eaten: ........................................

Food:...................................................................................................................................................
.............................................................................................................................................................
.............................................................................................................................................................

**Snack**

Time eaten: ........................................

Food:...................................................................................................................................................
.............................................................................................................................................................

**Dinner**

Time eaten: ........................................

Food:...................................................................................................................................................
.............................................................................................................................................................
.............................................................................................................................................................

**Exercise**: ............................................................................................................................................
.............................................................................................................................................................

**Quality of day out of 10**.....................................................................................................................

## J is for...

### Jams/Jelly

As all jams contain high amounts of both fructose and sucrose, eat it in moderation. There are some jams which do not contain any added sucrose or sugar substitutes such as St Dalfour Jams. Try and combine jam with some protein when you eat it. For example, a teaspoon of jam in plain live yoghurt, or a ryvita with cheese or cold meat with a little jam on the top. The sweet and savoury of jam and cheese/meat is delicious. Avoid low sugar or diabetic jams, they contain artificial sweeteners.

# DAY 52

**TODAYS DATE** ...........................................................................................................................................................

**Quality of sleep:** ...........................**Number of hours slept**: ...........................................................................
Scale: 1 = poor  Scale: 10 = deep and refreshing

**Vitality factor in morning** (scale 1= very tired, hungover, not well, dying)
(scale: 10 = full of energy, clear headed, refreshed, generally fantastic) ...................................................out of 10

**Breakfast**

Time eaten: ...........................................
Food:...........................................................................................................................................................
...........................................................................................................................................................

**Snack**

Time eaten: ...........................................
Food:...........................................................................................................................................................
...........................................................................................................................................................

**Lunch**

Time eaten: ...........................................
Food:...........................................................................................................................................................
...........................................................................................................................................................
...........................................................................................................................................................

**Snack**

Time eaten: ...........................................
Food:...........................................................................................................................................................
...........................................................................................................................................................

**Dinner**

Time eaten: ...........................................
Food:...........................................................................................................................................................
...........................................................................................................................................................
...........................................................................................................................................................

**Exercise**: ...........................................................................................................................................................
...........................................................................................................................................................

**Quality of day out of 10**...........................................................................................................................................

## K is for...

### Kinesiology

Viewed as a system of holistic natural healing, Kinesiology can help you know your body and maintain energy balancing. It can assess a person's nutritional status, including food intolerances and deficiencies.

Kinesiology is defined primarily as the use of non-invasive muscle testing to identify imbalances in the body's structural, chemical, emotional and energy levels.

The fundamental premise is that the body has innate energy, and these energy flows can be evaluated by testing the function of the muscles as a reflection of the body's overall balance. Hence it is not pure muscle strength that is being measured, but rather how the nervous system controls its muscles functions and energy flows within the body.

There are many different branches and areas of specialisation in kinesiology. Most practitioners will specialise in one main area such as emotional work, muscle rebalancing or nutrition, though they will have a good basic training in all areas. Search the web for further information on kinesiology or Touch For Health in your country.

**TODAYS DATE** ..........................................................................................................................................................................

**Quality of sleep:** ...............................**Number of hours slept**: ..................................................................................
Scale: 1 = poor  Scale: 10 = deep and refreshing

**Vitality factor in morning**  (scale 1= very tired, hungover, not well, dying)
(scale: 10 = full of energy, clear headed, refreshed, generally fantastic) .........................................................out of 10

**Breakfast**

Time eaten: .............................................
Food:.......................................................................................................................................................................
...............................................................................................................................................................................

**Snack**

Time eaten: .............................................
Food:.......................................................................................................................................................................
...............................................................................................................................................................................

**Lunch**

Time eaten: .............................................
Food:.......................................................................................................................................................................
...............................................................................................................................................................................
...............................................................................................................................................................................

**Snack**

Time eaten: .............................................
Food:.......................................................................................................................................................................
...............................................................................................................................................................................

**Dinner**

Time eaten: .............................................
Food:.......................................................................................................................................................................
...............................................................................................................................................................................
...............................................................................................................................................................................

**Exercise**: ...............................................................................................................................................................
...............................................................................................................................................................................

**Quality of day out of 10**.................................................................................................................................................

## L is for...

### Lactose intolerance

Lactose is a type of sugar found in cows milk. Some people have difficulty digesting it because they lack the digestive enzyme called lactase, which breaks it down into simple sugar in the stomach. Most 'A blood types, about 60% of 'O' blood types and a very small percentage of 'B' and 'AB' blood types, lack this enzyme. From childhood, many of them will experience discomfort, bloating, gas and sometimes pain when they consume milk. Live yoghurt can usually be tolerated because the lactose is broken down by the bacteria in yoghurt, making it more digestible. Cream is pure fat from milk and does not contain lactose. Many full milk cheeses will also cause problems for those intolerant to lactose, but some of the cheeses made with a high whey or protein content, such as feta, mozzarella and halloumi may be fine. Goat, sheep and camel milk are lactose free and therefore both the milk and cheeses are good substitutes. Lactose free cows milk is sometimes available in health shops and many supermarkets. Other milk substitutes include rice milk, oat milk, almond milk and soy milk. Please see entry on soya before taking this substitute regularly.

# DAY 54

**TODAYS DATE** ....................................................................................................................................................................................

**Quality of sleep:** ...................................**Number of hours slept**: ..............................................................................
Scale: 1 = poor  Scale: 10 = deep and refreshing

**Vitality factor in morning** (scale 1= very tired, hungover, not well, dying)
(scale: 10 = full of energy, clear headed, refreshed, generally fantastic) .........................................................................out of 10

**Breakfast**
Time eaten: ........................................
Food:..............................................................................................................................................................................
..................................................................................................................................................................................

**Snack**
Time eaten: ........................................
Food:..............................................................................................................................................................................
..................................................................................................................................................................................

**Lunch**
Time eaten: ........................................
Food:..............................................................................................................................................................................
..................................................................................................................................................................................
..................................................................................................................................................................................

**Snack**
Time eaten: ........................................
Food:..............................................................................................................................................................................
..................................................................................................................................................................................

**Dinner**
Time eaten: ........................................
Food:..............................................................................................................................................................................
..................................................................................................................................................................................
..................................................................................................................................................................................

**Exercise**: ........................................................................................................................................................................
..................................................................................................................................................................................

**Quality of day out of 10**................................................................................................................................................

**TODAYS DATE** ..............................................................................................................................................................................

**Quality of sleep:** ...................................**Number of hours slept**: ............................................................................................

Scale: 1 = poor  Scale: 10 = deep and refreshing

**Vitality factor in morning** (scale 1= very tired, hungover, not well, dying)

(scale: 10 = full of energy, clear headed, refreshed, generally fantastic) ...............................................out of 10

**Breakfast**

Time eaten: ............................................

Food:.......................................................................................................................................................

...............................................................................................................................................................

**Snack**

Time eaten: ............................................

Food:.......................................................................................................................................................

...............................................................................................................................................................

**Lunch**

Time eaten: ............................................

Food:.......................................................................................................................................................

...............................................................................................................................................................

...............................................................................................................................................................

**Snack**

Time eaten: ............................................

Food:.......................................................................................................................................................

...............................................................................................................................................................

**Dinner**

Time eaten: ............................................

Food:.......................................................................................................................................................

...............................................................................................................................................................

...............................................................................................................................................................

**Exercise**: ...............................................................................................................................................

...............................................................................................................................................................

**Quality of day out of 10**.........................................................................................................................

# DAY 56

**TODAYS DATE** ...............................................................................................................................................................

**Quality of sleep:** ...............................**Number of hours slept**: .................................................................

Scale: 1 = poor  Scale: 10 = deep and refreshing

**Vitality factor in morning** (scale 1= very tired, hungover, not well, dying)

(scale: 10 = full of energy, clear headed, refreshed, generally fantastic) ...................................................out of 10

**Breakfast**

Time eaten: ...........................................

Food:........................................................................................................................................................

............................................................................................................................................................

**Snack**

Time eaten: ...........................................

Food:........................................................................................................................................................

............................................................................................................................................................

**Lunch**

Time eaten: ...........................................

Food:........................................................................................................................................................

............................................................................................................................................................

............................................................................................................................................................

**Snack**

Time eaten: ...........................................

Food:........................................................................................................................................................

............................................................................................................................................................

**Dinner**

Time eaten: ...........................................

Food:........................................................................................................................................................

............................................................................................................................................................

............................................................................................................................................................

**Exercise**: ..............................................................................................................................................

............................................................................................................................................................

**Quality of day out of 10**.......................................................................................................................

## M is for...

### Margarines

Do not eat any of them. The manufacturing process of margarine and the chemicals that they are made with would make your hair stand on end. They contain indigestible hydrogenated acids which are far more harmful than the benefits they purport to give. Use only real butter which contains a short chain fatty acid that is very good for you or Olive oil spreads. A great better butter recipe is to mix a 450g packet of real butter, with a cup of virgin cold pressed olive oil. Mash together, put in a container and keep in the fridge for a soft, natural, nutrient rich, delicious spread. Use often in moderation.

### Meat

Meat generally has had negative press for the last 30 years and many of us wrongly believe that it is bad for us, particularly red meats. Meat is one of our oldest foods, our ancestors ate a diet comprised of around 80% meat for thousands of years and to think we haven't evolved into eating it makes mockery of the evolution theory! The 'A' blood type does struggle to digest red meat as they genetically lack sufficient hydrochloric acid digestive enzyme to break it down, evolving as they did when humans began to live in communities with a more agrarian, grain based diet. Whereas an 'O' or 'B' blood type will digest a 6oz steak in 4 to 6 hours before it passes completely into the small intestine, the 'A' blood type may take ten or more hours, causing putrification and gas to be produced in the gut. Many 'A' blood types report feeling heavy and gassy after eating red meat and naturally stay away from it. The studies that reported a strong link with red meat to bowel cancer, did not account for either the blood type breakdown of their test groups, or for the intake of modern hybrid wheat products, which my case studies of bowel diseases indicate are a major causative factor in many bowel disorders, but has not to date been taken into consideration in studies.

Most 'O' and 'B' blood types have asked for red meat 4 times a week, around 4-5oz/110-140g at a time for women and 5-6oz/140-170g for men. Our mistake is to eat too much at one sitting. Only well built active men can actually use the normal restaurant serving of 8-10oz/220-250g of red meat at one meal. (1oz of meat contains only 7-8g of usable protein). Our bodies will usually

**WEIGH AND MEASURE DAY**

weight...................... kgs/lbs
waist .............................. cm
hips ............................... cm
bust/chest ...................... cm
top of thigh..................... cm
top of arm ..................... cm
knee ............................. cm
calf............................... cm

### Weekly marks out of 10

Sleep quality .......................
Average no hours slept..........
AM vitality factor..................
Quality of week ....................
Adherence to programme.......
No of days exercised ...........

### NOTES AND OBSERVATIONS

...................................................
...................................................
...................................................
...................................................
...................................................
...................................................

# DAY 57

**TODAYS DATE** ...........................................................................................................................................................

**Quality of sleep:** ...............................**Number of hours slept**: ...........................................................................

Scale: 1 = poor  Scale: 10 = deep and refreshing

**Vitality factor in morning** (scale 1= very tired, hungover, not well, dying)

(scale: 10 = full of energy, clear headed, refreshed, generally fantastic) ...............................................................out of 10

**Breakfast**

Time eaten: ..........................................

Food:.........................................................................................................................................................

.................................................................................................................................................................

**Snack**

Time eaten: ..........................................

Food:.........................................................................................................................................................

.................................................................................................................................................................

**Lunch**

Time eaten: ..........................................

Food:.........................................................................................................................................................

.................................................................................................................................................................

.................................................................................................................................................................

**Snack**

Time eaten: ..........................................

Food:.........................................................................................................................................................

.................................................................................................................................................................

**Dinner**

Time eaten: ..........................................

Food:.........................................................................................................................................................

.................................................................................................................................................................

.................................................................................................................................................................

**Exercise**: .................................................................................................................................................

.................................................................................................................................................................

**Quality of day out of 10**.............................................................................................................................

only need 40-45g of protein at a time and the excess puts strain on the liver, which then produces protein toxins called ketones. The excess is then turned to fat. Eat little and often if you are not an A blood type.

The threat of BSE and the high use of hormone and antibiotics in meat is also a serious consideration. Buy organic whenever possible, it is worth every penny.

As the population of our planet increases, I feel it is everyone's responsibility to consume only what we really need, the cost of producing meat is very high in terms of land use and though many of us benefit from a little red meat often, excess is not only bad for us, but ultimately bad for the planet.

**Menopause**
I have over 150 women clients currently taking natural Hormone Replacement Therapy (HRT) in the form of Wild Yam, Dong Quai and Black Cohosh capsules. These natural herb substitutes for low progesterone and oestrogen have no side effects and are used by the body as required, meaning any excess is eliminated if not needed. All the women in full menopause are taking 1500mg daily of Wild Yam to replace the progesterone and *either* 80mg of Dong Quai *or* Black Cohosh, well above the current recommended doses which are not strong enough to have any effect. Women who have tried the herbs but have not taken enough therefore think they don't work, and as a result, have not seen the incredible benefits of these herbs. To date, very few if any full studies, have been carried out on natural HRT and a required dosage has never been established properly. The body has repeatedly insisted on this dosage in my clients and the benefits have been wonderful with no reported adverse effects. The last two herbs must not be taken together as the body says they cancel each other out. You will either be a Dong Quai or a Black Cohosh person, never both. Without personal testing I would recommend you begin the programme with Wild Yam and Dong Quai. If Don Quai is right for you, you will feel much better within three weeks. If you feel no real improvement or even a worsening of your symptoms, continue the Wild Yam but stop the Dong Quai. Wait three days and then start the Black Cohosh. One of them will work wonders for 99% of you. I have only had 2 ladies whose bodies have actually preferred the chemical HRT. When we tried the cream options, most women found them to be less effective

# DAY 58

**TODAYS DATE** ................................................................................................................................

**Quality of sleep:** ...................................**Number of hours slept**: ........................................

Scale: 1 = poor  Scale: 10 = deep and refreshing

**Vitality factor in morning** (scale 1= very tired, hungover, not well, dying)

(scale: 10 = full of energy, clear headed, refreshed, generally fantastic) ...............................................................out of 10

**Breakfast**

Time eaten: ...........................................

Food:.............................................................................................................................

........................................................................................................................

**Snack**

Time eaten: ...........................................

Food:.............................................................................................................................

........................................................................................................................

**Lunch**

Time eaten: ...........................................

Food:.............................................................................................................................

........................................................................................................................

........................................................................................................................

**Snack**

Time eaten: ...........................................

Food:.............................................................................................................................

........................................................................................................................

**Dinner**

Time eaten: ...........................................

Food:.............................................................................................................................

........................................................................................................................

........................................................................................................................

**Exercise**: ....................................................................................................................

........................................................................................................................

**Quality of day out of 10**................................................................................................

and prefer the capsules. Sage Tea is also excellent for stopping hot flushes. Women beginning menopause can take half the above dose for the first year at the first sign of symptoms. This programme is highly effective in preventing all the downfalls of menopause such as loss of bone density, hair and muscle loss and dryness. The herbs can be continued over all the menopausal years without any fear of side effects.

I would also not recommend using soya products unless you have Japanese, Chinese or South American ancestry. Please see the entry on Soya for more information.

## Milk

Buy organic if you can! Non-organic milk does unavoidably contain hormones and antibiotics, given to cows. 90% of the 'B' blood type and 40% of the 'O' blood group have no problem digesting the lactose and caseine in milk and are fine with dairy products. If you are dairy intolerant it is unusual that you would enjoy drinking milk. If you are intolerant to milk, you will be fine eating butter (which is the fat in milk) and yoghurt, where the bacteria has already broken down the lactose for you.

Skimmed milk (less than 1% fat) is not good for you! In order to digest the fat and protein in milk, bile from the liver must be triggered into the stomach, to break it down fully and absorb the calcium and nutrients from the milk. Skimmed milk contains so little fat that the bile is not triggered, leading to incomplete digestion. If you are drinking skimmed milk or eating fat free cheeses, thinking you are getting your calcium… you are not! Semi-skimmed milk, naturally low fat cheeses such as feta and halloumi and low fat cottage cheese and cheddars are ideal, they containing just enough fat to digest all their nutrients completely.

## Millet

Millet is an ancient grain, which is gluten free. Millet grain is one of the smallest of all cultivated grain and makes a delicious breakfast porridge when cooked in milk or water. It can also be used in soups, breakfast cereals and pancakes. Some anthropologists believe that this 8,000 year-old grain was our first agricultural crop. It is a nutritious grain with a high complex carbohydrate content.

### NOTES AND OBSERVATIONS

...................................
...................................
...................................
...................................
...................................
...................................
...................................
...................................
...................................
...................................
...................................
...................................
...................................
...................................
...................................
...................................
...................................
...................................
...................................
...................................
...................................
...................................
...................................
...................................
...................................
...................................
...................................
...................................
...................................
...................................

**TODAYS DATE** ..............................................................................................................................................................

**Quality of sleep:** ................................**Number of hours slept**: ....................................................................

Scale: 1 = poor  Scale: 10 = deep and refreshing

**Vitality factor in morning** (scale 1= very tired, hungover, not well, dying)

(scale: 10 = full of energy, clear headed, refreshed, generally fantastic) ...........................................out of 10

**Breakfast**

Time eaten: .................................................

Food:.........................................................................................................................................................

.................................................................................................................................................................

**Snack**

Time eaten: .................................................

Food:.........................................................................................................................................................

.................................................................................................................................................................

**Lunch**

Time eaten: .................................................

Food:.........................................................................................................................................................

.................................................................................................................................................................

.................................................................................................................................................................

**Snack**

Time eaten: .................................................

Food:.........................................................................................................................................................

.................................................................................................................................................................

**Dinner**

Time eaten: .................................................

Food:.........................................................................................................................................................

.................................................................................................................................................................

.................................................................................................................................................................

**Exercise**: .................................................................................................................................................

.................................................................................................................................................................

**Quality of day out of 10**.......................................................................................................................

## N is for...

### Neck Pain

Believe it or not your food intolerances may be a major cause of your neck pain and tension. The muscles in the neck are connected to the stomach by your stomach meridian or energy line. When you eat a food which you have difficulty digesting and are intolerant to, the flow of energy to the meridian line is inhibited. If you are eating this food regularly or in sudden excess, the meridian line becomes blocked. As a direct result the muscle which this energy meridian controls, goes into deep spasm. In extreme cases this causes what is medically known as wry neck, where one side of your neck becomes so tight, that you are unable to move your head without a great deal of pain. Several years ago a professional golfer came to see me with this condition that was not responding to more than two weeks of physiotherapy and treatment. His body told me that it was directly due to eating too much lobster! He admitted in amazement that he had recently returned from a tournament in Asia where the best and most plentiful food on offer had been langoustine. He had eaten them consistently for a week. His neck began to tighten towards the end of the week. Since returning he had continued his shellfish binge with regular meals of his favourite king prawns. His neck muscles were experiencing FISS, Food Intolerance Shock Syndrome (my coined phrase). After a few days of very high doses of vitamin C to absorb the toxins and avoiding all shellfish, his condition improved and disappeared. The relationship between the food and his neck could have seriously affected his career as it would have steadily got worse and more sensitive over the years.

The most common cause of FISS is wheat, but I have also seen it caused by lettuce, tomatoes, chicken, tea, coffee, oranges and tropical fruit. Food intolerances can also directly inflame the spine, causing pain in any part of the back. They will particularly attack any area of the spine that is weakened through trauma or thinning of the discs. These weaknesses will often appear to be the cause, but the pain remains even if the weakness is treated. If you suffer from a bad neck or back, which does not respond to treatment, try a strict avoidance programme of all your blood intolerances and the above list of foods. Reintroduce each of the foods one by one, once the pain has receded from the detox. This will pinpoint which foods are the culprits.

# DAY 60

**TODAYS DATE** .............................................................................................................................................................

**Quality of sleep:** ...............................**Number of hours slept**: .........................................................................

Scale: 1 = poor  Scale: 10 = deep and refreshing

**Vitality factor in morning** (scale 1= very tired, hungover, not well, dying)

(scale: 10 = full of energy, clear headed, refreshed, generally fantastic) ...........................................................out of 10

## Breakfast

Time eaten: .............................................

Food:.............................................................................................................................................................

.............................................................................................................................................................

## Snack

Time eaten: .............................................

Food:.............................................................................................................................................................

.............................................................................................................................................................

## Lunch

Time eaten: .............................................

Food:.............................................................................................................................................................

.............................................................................................................................................................

.............................................................................................................................................................

## Snack

Time eaten: .............................................

Food:.............................................................................................................................................................

.............................................................................................................................................................

## Dinner

Time eaten: .............................................

Food:.............................................................................................................................................................

.............................................................................................................................................................

.............................................................................................................................................................

**Exercise**: .....................................................................................................................................................

.............................................................................................................................................................

**Quality of day out of 10**.................................................................................................................................

**O is for...**

### Oranges

Surprisingly, oranges are one of the most common food intolerances in all the blood types. The orange turns acidic when it is in the stomach whereas the lemon and lime become alkaline during digestion. The 'O' blood type in particular finds oranges very acidic and they are a common cause of heartburn and discomfort but also occur frequently as a contributing food causing arthritis and joint ache. My advice in the light of the huge percentage of my clients I have tested who cannot tolerate oranges (around 80%) is to switch to less acidic citrus fruit such as grapefruit or to other juices such as pineapple. A good general rule to follow is to always dilute juices by half to two thirds with water. This will reduce the amount of sugar and calories that are contained in freshly squeezed and concentrated fruit juices. Lemon and lime will neutralize acidity in the stomach and are excellent digestives. Squeeze half a lemon into a cup of water to cleanse the system first thing in the morning or after a meal if you are prone to indigestion.

### Organic Foods

Certified organic foods contain no synthetic pesticides or herbicides, no preservatives or additives, no genetically modified foods and no irradiation. They are grown using sustainable natural agricultural techniques that enrich the soil, improve farm biodiversity and have less soil erosion and ground water pollution.

Conventional agriculture uses millions of pounds of toxic chemicals. When synthetic pesticides and fertilizers were first used in North America, pests and weeds were virtually eradicated. Crop yields soared. Corn yields have risen from 26 bushels per acre in 1926 to 127 bushels in 1996. But since their widespread use in the 1940's the long-term effects of these toxins on our environment and health has become starkly apparent. Weeds and insects quickly developed resistance to the chemicals. Ever more powerful toxins were needed which have proved indiscriminate; killing everything they touched including the soil.

The accumulation of pesticide residues in foods, soil and ground water is now

# DAY 61

**TODAYS DATE** ...................................................................................................................................................

**Quality of sleep:** ...............................**Number of hours slept**: ..............................................................
Scale: 1 = poor  Scale: 10 = deep and refreshing

**Vitality factor in morning**  (scale 1= very tired, hungover, not well, dying)
(scale: 10 = full of energy, clear headed, refreshed, generally fantastic) ..........................................................out of 10

**Breakfast**

Time eaten: ...........................................

Food:.....................................................................................................................................................

.............................................................................................................................................................

**Snack**

Time eaten: ...........................................

Food:.....................................................................................................................................................

.............................................................................................................................................................

**Lunch**

Time eaten: ...........................................

Food:.....................................................................................................................................................

.............................................................................................................................................................

.............................................................................................................................................................

**Snack**

Time eaten: ...........................................

Food:.....................................................................................................................................................

.............................................................................................................................................................

**Dinner**

Time eaten: ...........................................

Food:.....................................................................................................................................................

.............................................................................................................................................................

.............................................................................................................................................................

**Exercise**: ..............................................................................................................................................

.............................................................................................................................................................

**Quality of day out of 10**.......................................................................................................................

suspected of being dangerous to our health. The US National Research Council concluded in 1993 that "some children were ingesting enough pesticides to harm them, even though their food was within Federal limits". American Congress passed The Food Quality Protection Act in 1996 to reassess the standards for pesticides in foods. The results have yet to be released.

In the meantime, be aware of your options and err if you can on the side of caution. Look for foods bearing a recognised "Certified" Organic stamp. These growers are inspected and certified annually to ensure compliance with all organic standards. They are required to maintain a complete paper trail from the farm to processing, proving that all ingredients come from organic sources.

## Osteoporosis

The following information is taken directly from the website of the National Institutes of Health for Osteoporosis research site and I feel is a vital area of information that we should all be aware of. If your bone test does show a lower or risk factor density level, please do not panic but keep this in perspective. There are many things you can do to help yourself prevent and possibly reverse the condition.

According to the US National Institutes of Health Osteoporosis and Related Bone Diseases Centre for Research, Osteoporosis or porous bones, is a disease characterised by low bone mass and structural deterioration of bone tissue, leading to bone fragility and an increased susceptibility to fractures of the hip, spine and wrist. Men as well as women suffer from osteoporosis, a disease that can be prevented and treated.

## The Body Talks

I have recently discovered that I have quite severe osteoporosis, age 35. My Body has told me that I have a genetic weakness of a liver enzyme (unspecified) that helps absorb calcium into my bones. I need to take 50mg of Zinc daily for life to support this enzyme which will then be able to regenerate my bone density. I am seeing this condition now quite often in clients and suspect it may be a common underlying reason why young people and families suffer with the disease. Two cases have already shown significant regeneration after taking the zinc for 10 months.

# DAY 62

**TODAYS DATE** ....................................................................................................................................................

**Quality of sleep:** ............................**Number of hours slept**: ................................................................

Scale: 1 = poor  Scale: 10 = deep and refreshing

**Vitality factor in morning** (scale 1= very tired, hungover, not well, dying)

(scale: 10 = full of energy, clear headed, refreshed, generally fantastic) ...........................................................out of 10

**Breakfast**

Time eaten: .........................................

Food:....................................................................................................................................................

.............................................................................................................................................................

**Snack**

Time eaten: .........................................

Food:....................................................................................................................................................

.............................................................................................................................................................

**Lunch**

Time eaten: .........................................

Food:....................................................................................................................................................

.............................................................................................................................................................

.............................................................................................................................................................

**Snack**

Time eaten: .........................................

Food:....................................................................................................................................................

.............................................................................................................................................................

**Dinner**

Time eaten: .........................................

Food:....................................................................................................................................................

.............................................................................................................................................................

.............................................................................................................................................................

**Exercise**: .............................................................................................................................................

.............................................................................................................................................................

**Quality of day out of 10**.......................................................................................................................

## What is Bone?

Bone is living, growing tissue. It is made mostly of collagen, a protein that provides a soft framework, and calcium phosphate, a mineral that adds strength and hardens the framework. This combination of collagen and calcium makes bone strong yet flexible to withstand stress. More than 99% of the body's calcium is contained in the bones and teeth. The remaining 1% is found in the blood.

Throughout your lifetime, old bone is removed (resorption) and new bone is added to the skeleton (formation). During childhood and teenage years, new bone is added faster than old bone is removed. As a result, bones become larger, heavier and denser. Bone formation continues at a pace faster than resorption until peak bone mass (maximum bone density and strength) is reached around age 30. After age 30, bone resorption slowly begins to exceed bone formation. Bone loss is most rapid in the first few years after menopause but persists into the postmenopausal years. Osteoporosis develops when bone resorption occurs too quickly or if replacement occurs too slowly. Osteoporosis is more likely to develop if you did not reach optimal bone mass during your bone building years.

## Risk Factors

Certain factors are linked to the development of osteoporosis or contribute to an individual's likelihood of developing the disease. These are called "risk factors."

### Risk factors you cannot change:

### Gender:
Your chances of developing osteoporosis are greater if you are a woman. Women have less bone tissue and lose bone more rapidly than men because of the changes involved in menopause.

### Age:
The older you are, the greater your risk of osteoporosis. Your bones become less dense and weaker as you age.

### Body size:
Small, thin-boned women are at greater risk.

# DAY 63

**TODAYS DATE** ...........................................................................................................................................................................

**Quality of sleep:** ............................**Number of hours slept**: ..........................................................................................
Scale: 1 = poor  Scale: 10 = deep and refreshing

**Vitality factor in morning**  (scale 1= very tired, hungover, not well, dying)
(scale: 10 = full of energy, clear headed, refreshed, generally fantastic) ...............................................................out of 10

**Breakfast**

Time eaten: ...........................................

Food:...........................................................................................................................................................................

...........................................................................................................................................................................

**Snack**

Time eaten: ...........................................

Food:...........................................................................................................................................................................

...........................................................................................................................................................................

**Lunch**

Time eaten: ...........................................

Food:...........................................................................................................................................................................

...........................................................................................................................................................................

...........................................................................................................................................................................

**Snack**

Time eaten: ...........................................

Food:...........................................................................................................................................................................

...........................................................................................................................................................................

**Dinner**

Time eaten: ...........................................

Food:...........................................................................................................................................................................

...........................................................................................................................................................................

...........................................................................................................................................................................

**Exercise**:...................................................................................................................................................................

...........................................................................................................................................................................

**Quality of day out of 10**.............................................................................................................................................

113

## Ethnicity:

Caucasian and Asian women are at highest risk. African-American and Latino women have a lower but still significant risk.

## Family history:

Susceptibility to fracture may be, in part, hereditary. People whose parents have a history of fractures also seem to have reduced bone mass and may be at risk of fractures.

**Risk factors you can change:**

## Sex hormones:

Abnormal absence of menstrual periods (amenorrhea), low oestrogen level (menopause) and low testosterone level in men.

● Anorexia

● A lifetime diet low in calcium and vitamin D

● A lifetime diet low in regular high quality protein

● Use of certain medications, such as glucocorticoids or some anticonvulsants

● An inactive lifestyle or extended bed rest

● Cigarette smoking

● Excessive use of alcohol

**Prevention:**

To reach optimal peak bone mass and continue building new bone tissue as you get older, there are several factors you should consider:

## Calcium:

An inadequate supply of calcium over the lifetime is thought to play a significant role in contributing to the development of osteoporosis. Many published studies show that low calcium intakes appear to be associated with low bone mass, rapid bone loss and high fracture rates. National nutrition surveys have shown that many people consume less than half the amount of calcium recommended

**WEIGH AND MEASURE DAY**

weight...................... kgs/lbs
waist ............................. cm
hips ............................... cm
bust/chest ....................... cm
top of thigh..................... cm
top of arm ...................... cm
knee .............................. cm
calf................................ cm

**Weekly marks out of 10**
Sleep quality .........................
Average no hours slept...........
AM vitality factor...................
Quality of week .....................
Adherence to programme.......
No of days exercised ............

NOTES AND OBSERVATIONS
.................................................
.................................................
.................................................
.................................................
.................................................
.................................................

**TODAYS DATE** .......................................................................................................................................................

**Quality of sleep:** .............................**Number of hours slept**: ...........................................................................

Scale: 1 = poor  Scale: 10 = deep and refreshing

**Vitality factor in morning**  (scale 1= very tired, hungover, not well, dying)

(scale: 10 = full of energy, clear headed, refreshed, generally fantastic) ........................................................out of 10

**Breakfast**

Time eaten: .........................................

Food:..............................................................................................................................................................

.......................................................................................................................................................................

**Snack**

Time eaten: .........................................

Food:..............................................................................................................................................................

.......................................................................................................................................................................

**Lunch**

Time eaten: .........................................

Food:..............................................................................................................................................................

.......................................................................................................................................................................

.......................................................................................................................................................................

**Snack**

Time eaten: .........................................

Food:..............................................................................................................................................................

.......................................................................................................................................................................

**Dinner**

Time eaten: .........................................

Food:..............................................................................................................................................................

.......................................................................................................................................................................

.......................................................................................................................................................................

**Exercise**: .....................................................................................................................................................

.......................................................................................................................................................................

**Quality of day out of 10**.............................................................................................................................

to build and maintain healthy bones. Good sources of calcium include low fat dairy products, such as milk, yogurt, cheese and ice cream; dark green, leafy vegetables, such as broccoli, collard greens, bok choy and spinach; sardines and salmon with bones, tofu, almonds and foods fortified with calcium, such as orange juice, cereals and breads. Depending upon how much calcium you get each day from food, you may need to take a calcium supplement.

According to the body's information about the intake of calcium however, it appears that calcium supplements may do more harm than good when taken in simple calcium supplement form. Please see entry on Calcium for more information.

Calcium requirements change during one's lifetime. The body's demand for calcium is greater during childhood and adolescence, when the skeleton is growing rapidly, and during pregnancy and breastfeeding. Postmenopausal women and older men also need to consume more calcium. This may be caused by inadequate amounts of vitamin D, which is necessary for intestinal absorption of calcium. Also, as you age, your body becomes less efficient at absorbing calcium and other nutrients. Older adults are more likely to have chronic medical problems and to use medications that may impair calcium absorption.

### Vitamin D:
Vitamin D plays an important role in calcium absorption and in bone health. It is synthesized in the skin through exposure to sunlight. While many people are able to obtain enough vitamin D naturally, studies show that vitamin D production decreases in the elderly, in people who are housebound and during the winter. These individuals may require vitamin D supplementation to ensure a daily intake of between 400 to 800 IU of vitamin D. Massive doses are not recommended.

### Exercise:
Like muscle, bone is living tissue that responds to exercise by becoming stronger. The best exercise for your bones is weight-bearing exercise, that forces you to work against gravity. These exercises include walking, hiking, jogging, stair-climbing, weight training, tennis and dancing.

NOTES AND OBSERVATIONS

..................................
..................................
..................................
..................................
..................................
..................................
..................................
..................................
..................................
..................................
..................................
..................................
..................................
..................................
..................................
..................................
..................................
..................................
..................................
..................................
..................................
..................................
..................................
..................................
..................................
..................................
..................................
..................................
..................................
..................................

# DAY 65

**TODAYS DATE** ...........................................................................................................................................................................

**Quality of sleep:** ................................**Number of hours slept**: ..........................................................................................
Scale: 1 = poor  Scale: 10 = deep and refreshing

**Vitality factor in morning** (scale 1= very tired, hungover, not well, dying)
(scale: 10 = full of energy, clear headed, refreshed, generally fantastic) ..................................................................out of 10

**Breakfast**

Time eaten: ........................................
Food:...........................................................................................................................................................................
..................................................................................................................................................................................

**Snack**

Time eaten: ........................................
Food:...........................................................................................................................................................................
..................................................................................................................................................................................

**Lunch**

Time eaten: ........................................
Food:...........................................................................................................................................................................
..................................................................................................................................................................................
..................................................................................................................................................................................

**Snack**

Time eaten: ........................................
Food:...........................................................................................................................................................................
..................................................................................................................................................................................

**Dinner**

Time eaten: ........................................
Food:...........................................................................................................................................................................
..................................................................................................................................................................................
..................................................................................................................................................................................

**Exercise**: .....................................................................................................................................................................
..................................................................................................................................................................................

**Quality of day out of 10**..............................................................................................................................................

## Smoking:

Smoking is bad for your bones as well as for your heart and lungs. Women who smoke have lower levels of oestrogen compared to nonsmokers and frequently go through menopause earlier. Postmenopausal women who smoke may require higher doses of hormone replacement therapy and may have more side effects. Smokers may also absorb less calcium from their diets.

## Alcohol:

Regular consumption of 2 to 3 units a day of alcohol may be damaging to the skeleton, even in young women and men. Those who drink heavily are more prone to bone loss and fractures, both because of poor nutrition as well as increased risk of falling.

## Medications that cause bone loss:

The long-term use of glucocorticoids (medications prescribed for a wide range of diseases, including arthritis, asthma, Crohn's disease, lupus and other diseases of the lungs, kidneys and liver) can lead to a loss of bone density and fractures. Other forms of drug therapy that can cause bone loss include long-term treatment with certain antiseizure drugs, such as phenytoin (Dilantin®) and barbiturates, gonadotropin releasing hormone (GnRH) analogs used to treat endometriosis, excessive use of aluminum-containing antacids, certain cancer treatments and excessive thyroid hormone. It is important to discuss the use of these drugs with your physician and not to stop or alter your medication dose on your own.

## Prevention Medications:

Various medications are available for the prevention, as well as treatment of osteoporosis. Read on for section entitled "Therapeutic Medications".

## Symptoms:

Osteoporosis is often called the "silent disease" because bone loss occurs without symptoms. People may not know that they have osteoporosis until their bones become so weak that a sudden strain, bump or fall causes a hip fracture or a vertebra to collapse. Collapsed vertebra may initially be felt or seen in the form of severe back pain, loss of height or spinal deformities such as kyphosis or severely stooped posture.

# DAY 66

**TODAYS DATE** ...........................................................................................................................................................................

**Quality of sleep:** .............................**Number of hours slept**: ........................................................................................

Scale: 1 = poor  Scale: 10 = deep and refreshing

**Vitality factor in morning**  (scale 1= very tired, hungover, not well, dying)

(scale: 10 = full of energy, clear headed, refreshed, generally fantastic) ...........................................................out of 10

**Breakfast**

Time eaten: ......................................

Food: ..............................................................................................................................................................................

.........................................................................................................................................................................................

**Snack**

Time eaten: ......................................

Food: ..............................................................................................................................................................................

.........................................................................................................................................................................................

**Lunch**

Time eaten: ......................................

Food: ..............................................................................................................................................................................

.........................................................................................................................................................................................

.........................................................................................................................................................................................

**Snack**

Time eaten: ......................................

Food: ..............................................................................................................................................................................

.........................................................................................................................................................................................

**Dinner**

Time eaten: ......................................

Food: ..............................................................................................................................................................................

.........................................................................................................................................................................................

.........................................................................................................................................................................................

**Exercise**: ......................................................................................................................................................................

.........................................................................................................................................................................................

**Quality of day out of 10** ...............................................................................................................................................

## Detection:

Following a comprehensive medical assessment, your doctor may recommend that you have your bone mass measured. Bone mineral density (BMD) tests measure bone density in the spine, wrist and/or hip (the most common sites of fractures due to osteoporosis), while others measure bone in the heel or hand. These tests are painless, noninvasive and safe. Bone density tests can:

● Detect low bone density before a fracture occurs.
● Confirm a diagnosis of osteoporosis if you have already fractured.
● Predict your chances of fracturing in the future.
● Determine your rate of bone loss and/or monitor the effects of treatment if the test is conducted at intervals of a year or more.

*6-10 almonds eaten daily are recommended by our body's as the best form of calcium supplementation you can take. They contain high levels of calcium together with all the specific other nutrients such as potassium and magnesium in ideal ratio which together with the high level of good fats in the nuts also ensures that bile is released during digestion for optimum absorption. (Judy)*

## Therapeutic Medications:

Currently, oestrogen, calcitonin, alendronate, raloxifene and risedronate are approved by the U. S. Food and Drug Administration (FDA) for the treatment of postmenopausal osteoporosis. Oestrogen, alendronate, risedronate and raloxifene are approved for the prevention of the disease. Alendronate is approved for the treatment of osteoporosis in men. Alendronate and risedronate are approved for use by men and women with glucocorticoid-induced osteoporosis.

## Oestrogen:

Oestrogen replacement therapy (ERT) has been shown to reduce bone loss, increase bone density in both the spine and hip, and reduce the risk of hip and spinal fractures in postmenopausal women. ERT is administered most commonly in the form of a pill or skin patch and is effective even when started after age 70. When oestrogen is taken alone, it can increase a woman's risk of developing cancer of the uterine lining (endometrial cancer). To eliminate this

**TODAYS DATE** ...................................................................................................................................................

**Quality of sleep:** ...................................**Number of hours slept**: ...........................................................................

Scale: 1 = poor  Scale: 10 = deep and refreshing

**Vitality factor in morning** (scale 1= very tired, hungover, not well, dying)

(scale: 10 = full of energy, clear headed, refreshed, generally fantastic) ...............................................................out of 10

**Breakfast**

Time eaten: ........................................

Food:...................................................................................................................................................................

.............................................................................................................................................................................

**Snack**

Time eaten: ........................................

Food:...................................................................................................................................................................

.............................................................................................................................................................................

**Lunch**

Time eaten: ........................................

Food:...................................................................................................................................................................

.............................................................................................................................................................................

.............................................................................................................................................................................

**Snack**

Time eaten: ........................................

Food:...................................................................................................................................................................

.............................................................................................................................................................................

**Dinner**

Time eaten: ........................................

Food:...................................................................................................................................................................

.............................................................................................................................................................................

.............................................................................................................................................................................

**Exercise**: ........................................................................................................................................................

.............................................................................................................................................................................

**Quality of day out of 10**..................................................................................................................................

risk, physicians prescribe the hormone progesterone in combination with oestrogen (hormone replacement therapy or HRT) for those women who have not had a hysterectomy. ERT/HRT relieves menopause symptoms and has been shown to have beneficial effects on both the skeleton and heart.

Experts recommend ERT for women at high risk for osteoporosis. ERT is approved for both the prevention and treatment of osteoporosis. ERT is especially recommended for women whose ovaries were removed before age 50. Oestrogen replacement should also be considered by women who have experienced natural menopause and have multiple osteoporosis risk factors, such as early menopause, family history of osteoporosis or below normal bone mass for their age. As with all drugs, the decision to use oestrogen should be made after discussing the benefits and risks and your own situation with your doctor.

## Raloxifene:

Raloxifene (brand name "Evista") is a drug that is approved for the prevention and treatment of osteoporosis. It is from a new class of drugs called Selective Oestrogen Receptor Modulators (SERMs) that appear to prevent bone loss at the spine, hip and total body. Raloxifene has been shown to have beneficial effects on bone mass and bone turnover and can reduce the incidence of vertebral fractures by 30-50%. While side-effects are not common with raloxifene, those reported include hot flushes and deep vein thrombosis, the latter of which is also associated with oestrogen therapy. Additional research studies on raloxifene will be ongoing for several more years.

## Alendronate:

Alendronate (brand name "Fosamax") is a medication from the class of drugs called bisphosphonates. Like oestrogen and raloxifene, alendronate is approved for both the prevention and treatment of osteoporosis. Alendronate is also used to treat the bone loss from glucocorticoid medications like prednisone or cortisone and is approved for the treatment of osteoporosis in men. In postmenopausal women with osteoporosis, the bisphosphonate alendronate reduces bone loss, increases bone density in both the spine and hip and reduces the risk of both spine fractures and hip fractures. Side effects from alendronate are uncommon, but may include abdominal or musculoskeletal pain, nausea,

# DAY 68

**TODAYS DATE**...........................................................................................................................................................

**Quality of sleep:** ...................................**Number of hours slept**:...........................................................................
Scale: 1 = poor  Scale: 10 = deep and refreshing

**Vitality factor in morning**  (scale 1= very tired, hungover, not well, dying)
(scale: 10 = full of energy, clear headed, refreshed, generally fantastic) ........................................................out of 10

**Breakfast**

Time eaten: ........................................

Food:.....................................................................................................................................................................

...........................................................................................................................................................................

**Snack**

Time eaten: ........................................

Food:.....................................................................................................................................................................

...........................................................................................................................................................................

**Lunch**

Time eaten: ........................................

Food:.....................................................................................................................................................................

...........................................................................................................................................................................

...........................................................................................................................................................................

**Snack**

Time eaten: ........................................

Food:.....................................................................................................................................................................

...........................................................................................................................................................................

**Dinner**

Time eaten: ........................................

Food:.....................................................................................................................................................................

...........................................................................................................................................................................

...........................................................................................................................................................................

**Exercise**:...........................................................................................................................................................

...........................................................................................................................................................................

**Quality of day out of 10**...........................................................................................................................................

heartburn or irritation of the oesophagus. The medication should be taken on an empty stomach and with a full glass of water first thing in the morning. After taking alendronate, it is important to wait in an upright position for at least half an hour or preferably one hour, before the first food, beverage or medication of the day.

## Calcitonin:

Calcitonin is a naturally occurring non-sex hormone involved in calcium regulation and bone metabolism. In women who are at least 5 years beyond menopause, calcitonin slows bone loss, increases spinal bone density and according to anecdotal reports, relieves the pain associated with bone fractures. Calcitonin reduces the risk of spinal fractures and may reduce hip fracture risk as well. Studies on fracture reduction are ongoing. Calcitonin is currently available as an injection or nasal spray. While it does not affect other organs or systems in the body, injectable calcitonin may cause an allergic reaction and unpleasant side effects including flushing of the face and hands, urinary frequency, nausea and skin rash. The only side effect reported with nasal calcitonin is a runny nose.

## Risedronate:

Risedronate sodium (brand name Actonel®) is approved for the prevention and treatment of osteoporosis in postmenopausal women and for the prevention and treatment of glucocorticoid-induced osteoporosis in both men and women. Risedronate, a bisphosphonate, has been shown to slow or stop bone loss, increase bone mineral density and reduce the risk of spine and non-spine fractures. In clinical trials, side effects of risedronate were minimal to moderate and those that were reported occurred equally among people taking the medication and those taking a placebo. Risedronate should be taken with a glass of water at least 30 minutes before the first food or beverage of the day other than water. After taking risedronate, it is important to remain in an upright position and refrain from eating for at least 30 minutes.

NOTES AND OBSERVATIONS

# DAY 69

**TODAYS DATE** ...........................................................................................................................................

**Quality of sleep:** ...................................**Number of hours slept**: ...............................................................
Scale: 1 = poor  Scale: 10 = deep and refreshing

**Vitality factor in morning** (scale 1= very tired, hungover, not well, dying)
(scale: 10 = full of energy, clear headed, refreshed, generally fantastic) ........................................out of 10

**Breakfast**

Time eaten: ..........................................

Food:...........................................................................................................................................................
..............................................................................................................................................................

**Snack**

Time eaten: ..........................................

Food:...........................................................................................................................................................
..............................................................................................................................................................

**Lunch**

Time eaten: ..........................................

Food:...........................................................................................................................................................
..............................................................................................................................................................
..............................................................................................................................................................

**Snack**

Time eaten: ..........................................

Food:...........................................................................................................................................................
..............................................................................................................................................................

**Dinner**

Time eaten: ..........................................

Food:...........................................................................................................................................................
..............................................................................................................................................................
..............................................................................................................................................................

**Exercise**: ...............................................................................................................................................
..............................................................................................................................................................

**Quality of day out of 10**...........................................................................................................................

## TO MAINTAIN GOOD BONE DENSITY:

- Eat small amounts of protein at every meal
- Ensure your hormones remain balanced with the help of herbs or natural hormone replacement therapy
- Eat 6-10 almonds a day
- Do regular weight bearing exercise to stress the bones and encourage them to lay down more calcium. Walking actively for 40 minutes 4 times a week will ensure this
- Eat a balanced diet as described in this programme
- Maintain a healthy balance of fat in your diet, approximately 30% of calorie intake at each meal

## OVER-TRAINING:

There is a very fine line between getting fit and over-training, particularly in the early eager days of a new fitness programme. Exercise taken in excess for your current level of fitness will damage your immune system. When my clients come in to see me I always ask their body at what percentage level their immune system is functioning. This reflects the function of their adrenal glands that are responsible for some 300 different functions in the body including the immune system. If it is below 50% then I ask them NOT to exercise at all for the first one month of the detox. Until the burdens of the intolerances are lifted and the adrenals can begin to function again, any exercise is detrimental to their overall recovery. Once the glands begin to function above 50%, then gentle exercise can be introduced. The client also feels better and looks forward to exercising whereas undertaking a programme feeling like death warmed up, low in energy, motivation and overweight, is detrimental to both mind and body.

Life long weight loss and control is a healing issue. An exercise programme can damage your immune system further and it is vital that any programme starts off very slowly and gently for the first 2 months. That means a 40-minute walk with some stretching 4 times a week. When you are detoxed and have lost a few pounds of fat and fluid, you will begin to feel your vitality coming back and will actually want to get your body moving. This is the sign to slowly start to increase the intensity of the programme. Many exercise programmes are far too intensive

NOTES AND OBSERVATIONS

# DAY 70

**TODAYS DATE** ...........................................................................................................................................................

**Quality of sleep:** ...............................**Number of hours slept**: ......................................................................

Scale: 1 = poor  Scale: 10 = deep and refreshing

**Vitality factor in morning**  (scale 1= very tired, hungover, not well, dying)

(scale: 10 = full of energy, clear headed, refreshed, generally fantastic) .........................................................out of 10

**Breakfast**

Time eaten: ......................................

Food:...................................................................................................................................................................

...........................................................................................................................................................................

**Snack**

Time eaten: ......................................

Food:...................................................................................................................................................................

...........................................................................................................................................................................

**Lunch**

Time eaten: ......................................

Food:...................................................................................................................................................................

...........................................................................................................................................................................

...........................................................................................................................................................................

**Snack**

Time eaten: ......................................

Food:...................................................................................................................................................................

...........................................................................................................................................................................

**Dinner**

Time eaten: ......................................

Food:...................................................................................................................................................................

...........................................................................................................................................................................

...........................................................................................................................................................................

**Exercise**: .......................................................................................................................................................

...........................................................................................................................................................................

**Quality of day out of 10**................................................................................................................................

for most people to maintain a healthy immune system. Symptoms of over-training are colds and flu, tiredness and depression.

For suggested exercise regimes during the detox and weight healing stages, see "The Body Talks, Heal Your Weight".

## Overweight

Throw away those scales!! Overweight is a ratio of too much body fat for your height, build and muscle mass. Muscle is two and a half times heavier than fat but it also takes up much less volume. It is no good wanting to weigh under nine stone ladies if you have no muscle mass. You can still be underweight and flabby. Scales are both misleading and psychological killers. When on a weight loss programme, **ONLY** weigh yourself **ONCE** a week at the most, less if possible. Judge your weight loss by your clothes, your well being, your vitality factor and by what other people say. Reach a weight and size that makes you feel happy; at which good honest friends tell you, you look good. You may never have the type of body that will look like Cindy Crawford or David Beckham and life is too short to spend your precious days battling for the unattainable. Settle for healthy and fit, even if you carry up to five more pounds, that's two and a half more kilograms, than you or ideal social body norms, would have you be. And then stick to it. If you put on more than two pounds over this at any time of your life, immediately take action and lose it.

For those of you needing perhaps a little more incentive to lose weight, being obese when you are 40 knocks up to seven years off your life. Experts tracked the lives of 3,500 people over 50 years and found that overweight and obesity in adulthood are associated with large decreases in life expectancy. The magnitude of the loss is similar to that associated with smoking. Another study shows that the ten percent of women who are heaviest are 20 percent more likely to suffer breast cancer than the ten percent at the other end of the weight scale. (**Framington Heart Study**, Masssachusetts. Annals of Internal Medicine 7/1/03)

NOTES AND OBSERVATIONS

................................
................................
................................
................................
................................
................................
................................
................................
................................
................................
................................
................................
................................
................................
................................
................................
................................
................................
................................
................................
................................
................................
................................
................................
................................
................................
................................
................................
................................
................................
................................
................................
................................
................................

# DAY 71

**TODAYS DATE** ........................................................................................................................................................................

**Quality of sleep:** ...............................**Number of hours slept**: .............................................................................................
Scale: 1 = poor  Scale: 10 = deep and refreshing

**Vitality factor in morning**  (scale 1= very tired, hungover, not well, dying)
(scale: 10 = full of energy, clear headed, refreshed, generally fantastic) ...............................................................................out of 10

**Breakfast**

Time eaten: ...........................................

Food:.......................................................................................................................................................................
.............................................................................................................................................................................

**Snack**

Time eaten: ...........................................

Food:.......................................................................................................................................................................
.............................................................................................................................................................................

**Lunch**

Time eaten: ...........................................

Food:.......................................................................................................................................................................
.............................................................................................................................................................................
.............................................................................................................................................................................

**Snack**

Time eaten: ...........................................

Food:.......................................................................................................................................................................
.............................................................................................................................................................................

**Dinner**

Time eaten: ...........................................

Food:.......................................................................................................................................................................
.............................................................................................................................................................................
.............................................................................................................................................................................

**Exercise**: .............................................................................................................................................................................
.............................................................................................................................................................................

**Quality of day out of 10**...........................................................................................................................................................

## P is for...

### Potatoes

You may well ask why potatoes are so restricted when other starchy vegetables are allowed in small portions even in stage one of The Body Talks Programme. After all as long as the portions are small what does it matter if you have pumpkin, leeks, cooked carrots or…potato? You are right, it doesn't, if the potato eaten is truly the size of a golf ball and eaten always in its skin. A small potato will contain about three teaspoons of sugar. Unfortunately, the treasured potato does not contain the phytonutrients in the same concentration as other more colourful starchy vegetables.

Secondly, give an inch and too many of you take a mile. Heating the oven to bake a small baked potato hardly seems worth it, but if potato was allowed, it becomes too easy to justify perhaps a boiled, or even mashed, or worse still, roast spud. A potato cooked without its skin becomes acidic and loses a great deal of its fibre, making it quicker to digest and turn into sugar, therefore making it more fattening. The goodness of the potato is only found under the skin which is lost as soon as it is peeled. Because it is a basic staple of our diets, it is too difficult to limit it to that necessary small portion. Before long, a larger portion of peeled potato is a regular on your plate and the starch intake becomes too high during that all important first stage of your programme. So it is better banned until you have only a little weight left to lose.

As a general rule, never peel your potatoes even if you are going to mash, boil or roast them. Choose newer potatoes with thinner skins, scrub them well and cook them as if the skin were not there. Even roast potatoes, though perhaps lacking that fluffiness of peeled spuds, are still delicious, par boiled and then rolled in a little hot dripping and roasted in a hot oven, and only when you have reached stage three of the programme.

(1 small potato contains 15g carb = 3 tsp of white sugar)

### Peanuts

Most 'O' and 'B' blood group people are highly intolerant to this popular nut. The 'A' blood type loves it and it is a good form of protein for the born vegetarian, a type who needs non meat protein options. For the 'O' and 'B' blood types however, this nut can be very cancer forming and is best avoided where possible.

### WEIGH AND MEASURE DAY

weight...................... kgs/lbs
waist ............................. cm
hips ............................... cm
bust/chest ....................... cm
top of thigh ..................... cm
top of arm ...................... cm
knee .............................. cm
calf................................ cm

## Weekly marks out of 10

Sleep quality ........................
Average no hours slept...........
AM vitality factor ...................
Quality of week ....................
Adherence to programme.......
No of days exercised ...........

NOTES AND OBSERVATIONS
.............................................
.............................................
.............................................
.............................................
.............................................
.............................................

**TODAYS DATE** ...........................................................................................................................................................

**Quality of sleep:** ...........................**Number of hours slept**: ......................................................................

Scale: 1 = poor  Scale: 10 = deep and refreshing

**Vitality factor in morning** (scale 1= very tired, hungover, not well, dying)

(scale: 10 = full of energy, clear headed, refreshed, generally fantastic) ......................................................out of 10

**Breakfast**

Time eaten: ...........................................

Food:.............................................................................................................................................................

..................................................................................................................................................................

**Snack**

Time eaten: ...........................................

Food:.............................................................................................................................................................

..................................................................................................................................................................

**Lunch**

Time eaten: ...........................................

Food:.............................................................................................................................................................

..................................................................................................................................................................

..................................................................................................................................................................

**Snack**

Time eaten: ...........................................

Food:.............................................................................................................................................................

..................................................................................................................................................................

**Dinner**

Time eaten: ...........................................

Food:.............................................................................................................................................................

..................................................................................................................................................................

..................................................................................................................................................................

**Exercise**: ..................................................................................................................................................

..................................................................................................................................................................

**Quality of day out of 10**...........................................................................................................................

Peanuts are also covered in yeasts and quickly become rancid. Most commercial peanut butters are made from second-rate, damaged and fermented peanuts. They contain high levels of yeast mycotoxins and should be avoided by everyone. If your children love peanut butter, buy a more expensive quality make which should reflect the higher grade nuts used in the butter.

## Pulses

Pulses are highly nutritious and do not deserve their reputation as being highly fattening when eaten as part of a balanced diet. They should only be eaten in moderate portions because they are rich in calories and not easy to digest in large quantities for many people, but they are missing some of the 22 essential amino acids. To make a complete protein, if you are not eating meat at the same meal, they should be combined with a small quantity of brown or wild rice to ensure all 24 essential amino acids are eaten. Pulses contain two thirds carbohydrates to one third protein, which is why they are fairly high in calories, but because of their high fibre content, digest very slowly. If you are vegetarian and are eating pulses and legumes as your primary protein source, pulses and beans, combined with too much rice and grains, lead to a high carbohydrate meal, which triggers insulin. It is difficult for most vegetarians to stay slim on a high starch, pulses, legume and nut diet and they should try and limit their portions and substitute eggs and low fat cheeses with plenty of vegetables into their diets instead.

## Popcorn

Of all the snacks this one deserves its place in the dieters all time top ten of great fillers. Although corn is high in carbohydrate, popcorn loses calories in favour of volume. It is almost naturally fat free and is low in starch, making it a good snack option despite its negligible protein content. Neither does it contain many nutrients but one cup of popcorn will only give you 54 calories.

# DAY 73

**TODAYS DATE** ...............................................................................................................................................

**Quality of sleep:** .................................**Number of hours slept**: .....................................................

Scale: 1 = poor  Scale: 10 = deep and refreshing

**Vitality factor in morning**  (scale 1= very tired, hungover, not well, dying)

(scale: 10 = full of energy, clear headed, refreshed, generally fantastic) ...........................................................................................out of 10

**Breakfast**

Time eaten: ........................................

Food:.................................................................................................................................................

.........................................................................................................................................................

**Snack**

Time eaten: ........................................

Food:.................................................................................................................................................

.........................................................................................................................................................

**Lunch**

Time eaten: ........................................

Food:.................................................................................................................................................

.........................................................................................................................................................

.........................................................................................................................................................

**Snack**

Time eaten: ........................................

Food:.................................................................................................................................................

.........................................................................................................................................................

**Dinner**

Time eaten: ........................................

Food:.................................................................................................................................................

.........................................................................................................................................................

.........................................................................................................................................................

**Exercise**: .......................................................................................................................................

.........................................................................................................................................................

**Quality of day out of 10**.................................................................................................................

## Q is for…

### Quinoa

Quinoa (pronounces Keen-wa) is an ancient grain originally grown by the people of the Andes in South America. It is very low in gluten and has a delicious nutty flavour. Can be cooked as a porridge but is very high in starch as are all grains and should be eaten in moderation.

### Quitting

Up to you!! I think we all quit at some stage when the temptation of other foods become too great and we begin to cheat. Before long you are cheating daily and the slippery slope becomes a gushing stream. The pattern I observe most often in people is something like this… Start programme and avoid intolerances strictly for the first month, full of enthusiasm and keyed up to stay on it forever! Early results of less bloating, the loss of some pounds and an early burst of vitality, help ensure their efforts are rewarded. About 30% of people do not get this far! Of the 70% that do start and get beyond a month, 20% give up after a month, finding it too difficult and antisocial. They also tend to be the type of people who want miracle results and or need to fit in and not cause any inconvenience to people. A further 50% keep going and complete the initial 2-month full detox. They feel fantastic, look younger, have much more energy and have usually seen a significant alleviation of any food intolerant related symptoms such as skin problems, headaches, tummy problems or fatigue. Of this 50%, about 10% start to cheat too early and in introducing their food intolerances again, eat too many and find themselves back where they started within a month. About 40% continue strictly for a further month before carefully and slowly reintroducing foods in the process suggested and watching for reactions in the body. They have become accustomed to the balanced way of eating, have healed their systems and find that the foods they used to love, they no longer miss at all. They have lost body fat and have replaced this with muscle mass, feel more emotionally balanced and have reached a feeling of super health.

But we are all human. 99% of us, even those who achieved super health, quickly forget how we felt before and succumb to the delusion that we are now healed

# DAY 74

**TODAYS DATE** ....................................................................................................................................................

**Quality of sleep:** ...............................**Number of hours slept**: ..............................................................

Scale: 1 = poor  Scale: 10 = deep and refreshing

**Vitality factor in morning**  (scale 1= very tired, hungover, not well, dying)

(scale: 10 = full of energy, clear headed, refreshed, generally fantastic) ...........................................out of 10

**Breakfast**

Time eaten: ........................................

Food:.................................................................................................................................................................

.........................................................................................................................................................................

**Snack**

Time eaten: ........................................

Food:.................................................................................................................................................................

.........................................................................................................................................................................

**Lunch**

Time eaten: ........................................

Food:.................................................................................................................................................................

.........................................................................................................................................................................

.........................................................................................................................................................................

**Snack**

Time eaten: ........................................

Food:.................................................................................................................................................................

.........................................................................................................................................................................

**Dinner**

Time eaten: ........................................

Food:.................................................................................................................................................................

.........................................................................................................................................................................

.........................................................................................................................................................................

**Exercise**: ......................................................................................................................................................

.........................................................................................................................................................................

**Quality of day out of 10**..............................................................................................................................

and can eat anything in moderation. Before long we are eating too much, festive seasons arrive and we are tempted to eat everything we shouldn't, and it becomes a huge effort to get back to a balanced way of eating again. Most people, including myself, have completely stopped and restarted this programme several times, before we eventually learn our lesson and find it becomes a way of life. You never quit if you just never give up! Keep doing this until eventually it becomes more painful to do the wrong things, than to do the right. Hopefully it won't take a lifetime to achieve this!

**R is for...**

**Rice**

Like bread, when it comes to rice, you may as well sit on it. It will very quickly put excess pounds on your tummy and thighs. White rice is very fattening! All the goodness and fibre is removed from brown rice when it is refined into white rice. It is high in starch and low in nutrients. Two tablespoons of cooked white rice equals around thirty grams of carbohydrate or six teaspoons of white sugar. More often we will eat a minimum of four tablespoons of rice at a meal. Try and limit your rice intake at a meal to just one large tablespoon of white rice or two of brown. Always combine it with some fat, protein and vegetables to try and slow down the digestion of the sugar.

Brown rice contains four times the fibre and approximately two times the nutrients of white rice. Even though a cup of brown and white rice contain the same number of calories, the fibre in the brown rice slows down its digestion and the sugar is released into the blood more slowly, making it less likely to be turned to body fat.

Wild rice is a seed, not a grain and contains much higher levels of protein and 25% less carbohydrate and calories. It needs to be cooked for at least an hour until the seed bursts and opens out into a soft delicious food. Add a little fried onion, peppers, peas and corn for an excellent side dish to accompany any meal.

......................................
......................................
......................................
......................................
......................................
......................................
......................................
......................................
......................................
......................................
......................................
......................................
......................................
......................................
......................................
......................................
......................................
......................................
......................................
......................................
......................................
......................................
......................................
......................................
......................................
......................................
......................................
......................................
......................................
......................................
......................................
......................................

# DAY 75

**TODAYS DATE** .........................................................................................................................................................

**Quality of sleep:** ...................................**Number of hours slept**: .............................................................................

Scale: 1 = poor  Scale: 10 = deep and refreshing

**Vitality factor in morning** (scale 1= very tired, hungover, not well, dying)

(scale: 10 = full of energy, clear headed, refreshed, generally fantastic) .................................................................out of 10

**Breakfast**

Time eaten: ..........................................

Food:.....................................................................................................................................................................

.............................................................................................................................................................................

**Snack**

Time eaten: ..........................................

Food:.....................................................................................................................................................................

.............................................................................................................................................................................

**Lunch**

Time eaten: ..........................................

Food:.....................................................................................................................................................................

.............................................................................................................................................................................

.............................................................................................................................................................................

**Snack**

Time eaten: ..........................................

Food:.....................................................................................................................................................................

.............................................................................................................................................................................

**Dinner**

Time eaten: ..........................................

Food:.....................................................................................................................................................................

.............................................................................................................................................................................

.............................................................................................................................................................................

**Exercise**: ............................................................................................................................................................

.............................................................................................................................................................................

**Quality of day out of 10**..............................................................................................................................................

## Rye

Rye is a different grain from wheat and does contain a little gluten, so cannot be eaten if you are gluten intolerant. However, most rye is still in its natural original form and is an ideal substitute for people intolerant to just wheat. Ryvita is made with pure rye flour, water and salt. One ryvita contains 6 grams of slow digesting complex carbohydrate. Pure 100% rye bread is also an excellent complex carbohydrate and fibre source, eaten in small quantities of no more than 2 slices at a meal. Rye is high in potassium, necessary for regulating water balance within the body and so helping reduce fluid retention.

## S is for...

**Sugar...** See Carbohydrates

## Soya

Unless you have inherited Japanese or South American genetics, beware of soya and all soy products. This is a new food only introduced to the west in the last 20 years and 99% of western people I test for soy are highly intolerant to it. Your body has not been able to adjust and evolve into the very high level of natural hormones contained in this food. The 1% of westerners that I found could take soy all had some Japanese or South American ancestry, cultures which have eaten soya for centuries.

In 1999, two top scientists, working for the Food and Drug Administration in America, broke rank with their colleagues and wrote an internal protest letter, opposing the FDA's decision to approve a health claim that soya reduced the risk of heart disease. They warned of 28 studies disclosing the toxic effects of soya, revealing their studies had all produced significant and dangerous levels of breast cancer, brain damage and abnormalities in infants. In an interview with the Observer newspaper in the UK in August 1999, one of the soya experts, Daniel Doerge, said: 'Research has shown a clear link between soya and the potential for adverse effects in humans.' These studies were carried out on a western population. The studies that support the widely publicised benefits of taking soy, all result from longitudinal studies on people whose cultures have eaten soy

# DAY 76

**TODAYS DATE** ...............................................................................................................................................................

**Quality of sleep:** ...................................**Number of hours slept**: ..............................................................................
Scale: 1 = poor  Scale: 10 = deep and refreshing

**Vitality factor in morning** (scale 1= very tired, hungover, not well, dying)
(scale: 10 = full of energy, clear headed, refreshed, generally fantastic) ...............................................................out of 10

**Breakfast**

Time eaten: ...........................................

Food:..........................................................................................................................................................................

...........................................................................................................................................................................

**Snack**

Time eaten: ...........................................

Food:..........................................................................................................................................................................

...........................................................................................................................................................................

**Lunch**

Time eaten: ...........................................

Food:..........................................................................................................................................................................

...........................................................................................................................................................................

...........................................................................................................................................................................

**Snack**

Time eaten: ...........................................

Food:..........................................................................................................................................................................

...........................................................................................................................................................................

**Dinner**

Time eaten: ...........................................

Food:..........................................................................................................................................................................

...........................................................................................................................................................................

...........................................................................................................................................................................

**Exercise**: .................................................................................................................................................................

...........................................................................................................................................................................

**Quality of day out of 10**.............................................................................................................................................

products as a main part of their diets for hundreds of years. Yes, for them soy is beneficial and can protect against cancer. But for the westerner, the opposite is true. It is not just in vegetarian products such as tofu and soya milk that the danger lies. Soya is a key ingredient in products from meat sausages and fish fingers to salad creams and breakfast cereals. The soya industry, worth six billion dollars in the States each year alone, insists that the health benefits outweigh the risks. Richard Barnes, European director of the US Soy Bean Association said: "Millions of people around the world have been eating soya for years and have shown no signs of abnormalities". Have we? There can never be proof of my claim, but having tested so many people for soya and had it rejected 99% of the time, I am not convinced it is safe for Westerners with no history of soya in their blood. Add to this the fact much of it is now genetically modified. I strongly advise you avoid it until more is known about the long-term effects it may have on us, if we are ever going to be told the truth. This includes all soy products such as soy milk, tofu, soy sauce unless used very occasionally and soybeans. If you are vegetarian, use other seeds, nuts and pulses which are also high in protein and much safer.

Further studies have also indicated that a chemical found in soya may damage the sexual organs of boys in the womb and make them less fertile as adults. Pregnant women who eat soy could therefore be endangering their babies. A British scientific advisory panel warned that there is 'clear evidence' of a potential risk from soy-based formula milk for babies. The findings may help explain the growing incidence of infertility problems. The average sperm count of European males has dropped by a quarter in 25 years, and one in six couples in Britain now has difficulty conceiving.

**Saccharine**
See Aspartame

**Soy Sauce**
See Soya

**Spelt**
Spelt is original wheat, before it was selectively bred and modified into modern wheat. It contains approximately one third of the gluten found in modern wheat

## NOTES AND OBSERVATIONS

# DAY 77

**TODODAYS DATE** ..............................................................................................................................................................

**Quality of sleep:** ..............................**Number of hours slept**: ....................................................................................

Scale: 1 = poor  Scale: 10 = deep and refreshing

**Vitality factor in morning** (scale 1= very tired, hungover, not well, dying)

(scale: 10 = full of energy, clear headed, refreshed, generally fantastic) .........................................................out of 10

### Breakfast

Time eaten: ........................................

Food:........................................................................................................................................................................

............................................................................................................................................................................

### Snack

Time eaten: ........................................

Food:........................................................................................................................................................................

............................................................................................................................................................................

### Lunch

Time eaten: ........................................

Food:........................................................................................................................................................................

............................................................................................................................................................................

............................................................................................................................................................................

### Snack

Time eaten: ........................................

Food:........................................................................................................................................................................

............................................................................................................................................................................

### Dinner

Time eaten: ........................................

Food:........................................................................................................................................................................

............................................................................................................................................................................

............................................................................................................................................................................

**Exercise**: ................................................................................................................................................................

............................................................................................................................................................................

**Quality of day out of 10**............................................................................................................................................

and is highly digestible. Most people who are intolerant to wheat can eat spelt. A staple in biblical times, spelt makes a tasty nutty bread, which though heavier than modern bread due to the low gluten content, can be bought in specialist bakeries or made at home. It makes a delicious though crumbly pastry and is a good substitute in cakes and biscuits. It requires less water in recipes due to the lower gluten content. It is of course still starch and should be eaten in moderation. One slice of spelt bread contains 15 to 18grams of carbohydrate, although it is high in fibre and highly nutritious. See the Kenwood bread maker spelt bread recipe in The Body Talks- Heal Your Weight.

## Salt

Eat it in moderation by adding a little before and during cooking and very little to cooked food. If you live in a hot climate, our bodies perspire a great deal of water and salt and will naturally need more than if you live in a colder climate. Taste is a great indicator of how much salt you need. If it tastes very salty when you put some on your tongue, you do not need more. If it barely tastes salty, your body needs more. This can change almost daily.

Sodium functions with potassium to equalize the acid-alkali factor in the blood. Together they help regulate water balance within the body; that is to regulate the distribution of fluids on either side of the cell walls. Sodium and potassium are also involved in muscle contraction and expansion and in nerve stimulation. Because sodium and potassium must be in balance, the excessive use of salt depletes the body's conserves of its often scarce potassium supply. Alcohol, coffee, excessive sugar and carbonated drinks will increase the loss of potassium through the liver and increase urinary excretion, as will vomiting, severe malnutrition and stress, both mental and physical. A sodium deficiency is rare but can happen in the heat if too much water is taken without replacing the sodium. Sports drinks are strongly recommended if you are undertaking exercise in the heat for a prolonged period. A potassium deficiency may cause bloating, nervous disorders, insomnia, constipation, slow and irregular heartbeat and muscle damage. To ensure sufficient potassium intake eat plenty of green leafy vegetables, nuts and seeds, mint leaves, bananas if not an 'A' blood type and never peel a potato when you eat them, the potassium is just under the skin.

# DAY 78

**TODAYS DATE** ...............................................................................................................................................................................

**Quality of sleep:** .............................**Number of hours slept**: .........................................................................................

Scale: 1 = poor  Scale: 10 = deep and refreshing

**Vitality factor in morning** (scale 1= very tired, hungover, not well, dying)

(scale: 10 = full of energy, clear headed, refreshed, generally fantastic) .........................................................out of 10

**Breakfast**

Time eaten: .......................................

Food:.............................................................................................................................................................................

.......................................................................................................................................................................................

**Snack**

Time eaten: .......................................

Food:.............................................................................................................................................................................

.......................................................................................................................................................................................

**Lunch**

Time eaten: .......................................

Food:.............................................................................................................................................................................

.......................................................................................................................................................................................

.......................................................................................................................................................................................

**Snack**

Time eaten: .......................................

Food:.............................................................................................................................................................................

.......................................................................................................................................................................................

**Dinner**

Time eaten: .......................................

Food:.............................................................................................................................................................................

.......................................................................................................................................................................................

.......................................................................................................................................................................................

**Exercise**: ....................................................................................................................................................................

.......................................................................................................................................................................................

**Quality of day out of 10**...........................................................................................................................................

**Smoking .........say no more........**

Why worry about what you eat if you are going to voluntarily ingest not only nicotine, but also over 100 different toxic chemicals added to cigarettes by tobacco manufacturers! I think the greatest thing that would bother me, if I were a smoker, would be the realisation that since inhaling my first cigarette, I had not been in my right and normal state of mind from that moment! Nicotine would have ruled my life and my brain, from that moment onwards and all my actions, reactions, thoughts and emotions had been filtered through a drug and not through the clear conscious god given beauty of a clear clean mind. Nicotine alters the brain chemistry and causes a high. It takes approximately 20 minutes for the high from the nicotine in one cigarette to drop, after which you start to feel the need for another fix. This high is the addiction, meaning the low or the normal brain chemistry feels dull and depressing compared to this illusive buzz. You become agitated because you are not on a buzz and the so-called relaxation of the cigarette is not to bring your anxiety down, but to take it back up. The feeling of relaxation you immediately get from smoking the cigarette is the addiction being fed, but within minutes, its effects wear off and the anxiety begins all over again. Might not bother you…I can't imagine never knowing my true self…

Many tobaccos are also soaked in sugar solution to make them more addictive and sugar is actually much harder to give up as the brain becomes dependent on this quick low quality fuel and stops using the proper brain chemicals. If you are keen to give up and really mean it, you can help the cravings that result not just from nicotine withdrawal but also from the sugar, by using the amino acid L-Glutamine. The chemicals and sugar have replaced the brain's normal use of natural amino acids, particularly L-Glutamine, and cravings result in the early days when the brain is left without its fix and without its proper fuels to fill the gap. It may take several weeks for these amino acids to kick in and work properly again and in the meantime the sugar cravings can be unbearable, resulting in binge eating. It is quite safe and even advisable to take L-Glutamine to soften the withdrawal and increase your chance of success by taking up to 5000mg daily. Split the dosage into 1000mg doses and take every few hours between meals with water. Take it for 3 to 4 weeks and then gradually come off it over a period of about 10 days. If the cravings return, increase the amount for a while longer. It is also vital that you eat a balanced diet with regular protein to provide the body with the amino acids to repair your brain chemistry.

**WEIGH AND MEASURE DAY**

weight...................... kgs/lbs
waist ................................ cm
hips ................................. cm
bust/chest ....................... cm
top of thigh..................... cm
top of arm ...................... cm
knee .............................. cm
calf................................ cm

**Weekly marks out of 10**
Sleep quality .........................
Average no hours slept...........
AM vitality factor...................
Quality of week ....................
Adherence to programme.......
No of days exercised ............

NOTES AND OBSERVATIONS
..................................................
..................................................
..................................................
..................................................
..................................................
..................................................

**TODAYS DATE** ...............................................................................................................................................................................

**Quality of sleep:** ...........................**Number of hours slept**: ....................................................................

Scale: 1 = poor  Scale: 10 = deep and refreshing

**Vitality factor in morning** (scale 1= very tired, hungover, not well, dying)

(scale: 10 = full of energy, clear headed, refreshed, generally fantastic) ........................................................out of 10

**Breakfast**

Time eaten: .........................................

Food:..........................................................................................................................................................................
.................................................................................................................................................................................

**Snack**

Time eaten: .........................................

Food:..........................................................................................................................................................................
.................................................................................................................................................................................

**Lunch**

Time eaten: .........................................

Food:..........................................................................................................................................................................
.................................................................................................................................................................................
.................................................................................................................................................................................

**Snack**

Time eaten: .........................................

Food:..........................................................................................................................................................................
.................................................................................................................................................................................

**Dinner**

Time eaten: .........................................

Food:..........................................................................................................................................................................
.................................................................................................................................................................................
.................................................................................................................................................................................

**Exercise**: ..............................................................................................................................................................
.................................................................................................................................................................................

**Quality of day out of 10**..................................................................................................................................

**T is for...**

**Tofu**
See Soya

**Tea (see also herbal tea)**
Black tea tests negatively for 99% of 'O' and 'B' blood type clients that I test. Black teas include Breakfast tea, Earl Gray, Darjeeling, Indian tea, etc. It is not the caffeine but a protein in the tea leaf and the manufacturing process of black teas that these blood types strongly object to. For these blood types it is very toxic and I have observed that even one cup of tea a day, is enough to stop many of the 'O' and 'B' clients reaching full health. Try Rooibos tea, a tea from a different bush grown only in South Africa which tastes and brews very similarly to black tea, but contains no caffeine and is very low in tannin. It is high in antioxidants and is growing in popularity around the world for its health giving properties. It is sold as Rooibos or Red Bush tea in health shops all over the world. Many supermarkets now stock it as do some forward thinking hotels and restaurants. Green tea and herbal teas are also excellent.

**Turkey**
See Chicken

**TODAYS DATE** ...............................................................................................................................................................

**Quality of sleep:** ..............................**Number of hours slept**: ..................................................................
Scale: 1 = poor  Scale: 10 = deep and refreshing

**Vitality factor in morning**  (scale 1= very tired, hungover, not well, dying)
(scale: 10 = full of energy, clear headed, refreshed, generally fantastic) .................................................................out of 10

**Breakfast**

Time eaten: .........................................
Food:...............................................................................................................................................................
.........................................................................................................................................................................

**Snack**

Time eaten: .........................................
Food:...............................................................................................................................................................
.........................................................................................................................................................................

**Lunch**

Time eaten: .........................................
Food:...............................................................................................................................................................
.........................................................................................................................................................................
.........................................................................................................................................................................

**Snack**

Time eaten: .........................................
Food:...............................................................................................................................................................
.........................................................................................................................................................................

**Dinner**

Time eaten: .........................................
Food:...............................................................................................................................................................
.........................................................................................................................................................................
.........................................................................................................................................................................

**Exercise**: ........................................................................................................................................................
.........................................................................................................................................................................

**Quality of day out of 10**..............................................................................................................................

## U is for...

### Underweight

The programme designed by the body itself and explained in my book 'The Body Talks, Heal Your Weight' is about healing your weight, your endocrine glands and your brain chemistry. Because it is balanced, it allows your body to find its ideal weight over time, whether that means you need to lose it or put it on. The optimum nutrient intake of this programme, for life, will feed your body with vital nutrition without putting on fat, which particularly appeals to anyone suffering from an eating disorder such as anorexia or bulimia. I have had three very successful cases of young women over-coming their eating disorders using this system of eating. When they understood how the good food they were eating little and often, laid down muscle and not fat they were slowly able to increase their confidence in eating sufficient good nutrition. It is however vital that people suffering with eating disorders also receive counselling and support from a professional therapist.

For those of you who are simply unable to gain weight, and can eat and eat all sorts of carbohydrates, junk foods and sugar and never seem to put on an ounce, I feel for you. I understand that this can be as distressing as not being able to get thin. In every case I have seen, there has been an underlying health imbalance in either the gut or the endocrine system, particularly an overactive thyroid that switches up your metabolism and burns off calories at an astonishing rate. This may sound fantastic if you are overweight, but I can assure you it is not. Over active thyroid is usually accompanied by hyperactivity, followed by sudden collapses in energy, a wired but tired feeling constantly, mood swings and hair loss. In extreme cases, your eyeballs may appear more prominent. Please seek medical help if you suspect you may have this disorder.

# DAY 81

**TODAYS DATE** ...........................................................................................................................................................

**Quality of sleep:** ...............................**Number of hours slept**: .....................................................................

Scale: 1 = poor  Scale: 10 = deep and refreshing

**Vitality factor in morning** (scale 1= very tired, hungover, not well, dying)

(scale: 10 = full of energy, clear headed, refreshed, generally fantastic) ...................................................out of 10

## Breakfast

Time eaten: ...........................................

Food:....................................................................................................................................................

...........................................................................................................................................................

## Snack

Time eaten: ...........................................

Food:....................................................................................................................................................

...........................................................................................................................................................

## Lunch

Time eaten: ...........................................

Food:....................................................................................................................................................

...........................................................................................................................................................

...........................................................................................................................................................

## Snack

Time eaten: ...........................................

Food:....................................................................................................................................................

...........................................................................................................................................................

## Dinner

Time eaten: ...........................................

Food:....................................................................................................................................................

...........................................................................................................................................................

...........................................................................................................................................................

**Exercise**: .............................................................................................................................................

...........................................................................................................................................................

**Quality of day out of 10**............................................................................................................................

## V is for...

### Vinegar

Without being tested for yeast, it will be difficult to know whether or not you are intolerant to it. A good indication is if you like vinegar, particularly on fish and chips, you are tolerant to it! The more you dislike it, the more likely you are to be intolerant to it! All vinegars contain yeast, are highly acidic and even if you are fine with them, must be taken in moderation (as with everything!) The most beneficial of the vinegars is apple cider vinegar, which is made from cider which has already fermented most of the yeast. It is also well known to have medicinal properties, especially for arthritis, but this relationship is blood type linked. Put a little apple cider vinegar in a glass, fill up with hot water and add a teaspoon of honey for a lovely refreshing drink. The 'O' and 'B' types will rarely get the same benefits from drinking this concoction as do the 'A' and 'AB' types.

The rate at which you get drunk is also a good indication of yeast intolerance. If you are, you will be a "cheap date", yeast will affect you very quickly with just one glass of wine making you feel tipsy. You will also be prone to worse hangovers, to falling asleep soon after the initial high of getting drunk and to poor behaviour under the influence.

If you suspect you are intolerant to yeast, avoid all vinegars and substitute lemon juice in salad dressings.

### Vegetarian

I think many of us love the idea of vegetarianism for many reasons, not least because we are not killing animals. I tried to give up meat and fish but as a 'B' blood type, found my energy and strength dropped very quickly after just six weeks. We need protein and unless you are a dedicated cook and have the time to prepare carefully balanced meals which included plenty of non meat protein, you will pay the price. Your main options are cheese and eggs, pulses, nuts and seeds. White rice does not make up a complete protein and very few vegetarians I meet eat brown rice. You need however to eat sufficient protein three times a day to stay really healthy which gives you a very limited choice. More often that not, most vegetarians will eat an excess of pasta, rice, potato and bread and over time the low protein intake drops their metabolism and reduces their muscle mass. The excess starch turns to body fat and the inevitable

# DAY 82

**TODAYS DATE** ...........................................................................................................................................................

**Quality of sleep:** ...............................**Number of hours slept**: ......................................................................

Scale: 1 = poor  Scale: 10 = deep and refreshing

**Vitality factor in morning** (scale 1= very tired, hungover, not well, dying)

(scale: 10 = full of energy, clear headed, refreshed, generally fantastic) ...........................................out of 10

## Breakfast

Time eaten: ...................................

Food:.......................................................................................................................................................

.............................................................................................................................................................

## Snack

Time eaten: ...................................

Food:.......................................................................................................................................................

.............................................................................................................................................................

## Lunch

Time eaten: ...................................

Food:.......................................................................................................................................................

.............................................................................................................................................................

.............................................................................................................................................................

## Snack

Time eaten: ...................................

Food:.......................................................................................................................................................

.............................................................................................................................................................

## Dinner

Time eaten: ...................................

Food:.......................................................................................................................................................

.............................................................................................................................................................

.............................................................................................................................................................

**Exercise**: ...............................................................................................................................................

.............................................................................................................................................................

**Quality of day out of 10**..........................................................................................................................

result of this is weight gain or loss of vitality, not to mention a weakened immune system. The 'A' blood-type is the most successful of the blood-types as a vegetarian but they must still be very careful to ensure sufficient protein intake. Due to the danger soya products pose to our health for those of us not used to this powerful phytoestrogen in our culture, I believe that a dependency on soya as a protein substitute may be a time bomb. If you are a committed vegetarian, become very knowledgeable about cooking complete meals and ensure you make the time to do so regularly.

**Vegetables**
Fabulous, eat lots. We all know that but the reality can be quite different. Order extra when you are out for a meal, have a side salad, look for dishes with vegetables in them if you are not a big fan. When at home, try and choose several vegetables of different colours, as the colour represents different phyto-nutrients present in the vegetables. Each type of vegetable has its own benefits, vitamins and minerals, and by eating by colour, for example; a green one such as beans, leeks, spinach or brocolli, a red or orange one such as carrots, pumpkin, red peppers or butternut squash and a white one, such as parsnips or cauliflower, you will ensure the complete spectrum of nutrients are eaten. The cruciferous family of vegetables which include broccoli, cauliflower, cabbage and Chinese lettuce are known for their anti cancer properties and should be eaten in some form daily.

NOTES AND OBSERVATIONS

..................................
..................................
..................................
..................................
..................................
..................................
..................................
..................................
..................................
..................................
..................................
..................................
..................................
..................................
..................................
..................................
..................................
..................................
..................................
..................................
..................................
..................................
..................................
..................................
..................................
..................................
..................................
..................................
..................................
..................................
..................................

**TODAYS DATE** ........................................................................................................................................................

**Quality of sleep:** .............................**Number of hours slept**: ....................................................................

Scale: 1 = poor  Scale: 10 = deep and refreshing

**Vitality factor in morning**  (scale 1= very tired, hungover, not well, dying)

(scale: 10 = full of energy, clear headed, refreshed, generally fantastic) .......................................out of 10

**Breakfast**

Time eaten: ...........................................

Food:..................................................................................................................................................

........................................................................................................................................................

**Snack**

Time eaten: ...........................................

Food:..................................................................................................................................................

........................................................................................................................................................

**Lunch**

Time eaten: ...........................................

Food:..................................................................................................................................................

........................................................................................................................................................

........................................................................................................................................................

**Snack**

Time eaten: ...........................................

Food:..................................................................................................................................................

........................................................................................................................................................

**Dinner**

Time eaten: ...........................................

Food:..................................................................................................................................................

........................................................................................................................................................

........................................................................................................................................................

**Exercise**: .............................................................................................................................................

........................................................................................................................................................

**Quality of day out of 10**........................................................................................................................

## W is for...

### Water

The most commonly asked question about water is how much should I drink a day? There is no single answer to this. It depends on the weather, your activity level, your size and weight and how much water rich foods you are eating daily. Black tea and coffee are actually dehydrating for the body. A general good rule is to drink before you ever feel thirsty. In moderate climates and low activity this may be an 8oz glass of water every 2 to 3 hours, but in hotter climates try and drink a small glass every hour. Always keep water by your bed at night and have a glass before sleep and on waking up. A sign of dehydration that you are not drinking enough water is a mild headache over the eyes and a white furry tongue. When there is not enough water in your body, you produce less saliva to wash your tongue and the dead cells on your tongue are able to accumulate in a white film. Dry skin can be caused by dehydration though there are also many other reasons that this can occur such as hormonal imbalance, food intolerance build up, toxic build-up and malnutrition. When you are detoxing ensure you are drinking plenty of fresh still water every hour. Avoid drinking too much carbonated water, the fizziness alters the sodium potassium balance in your cells and can actually increase fluid retention. Drink only three to four times a week.

### Wine

I know...we've all heard how a glass of wine a day is good for the heart and the blood and in a few lucky individuals who are not intolerant to yeast, alcohol and grapes, I am sure it is true. But on average, 80% of the bodies I have asked about this have disagreed. Many people are intolerant to one or more of the elements that go into making wine which means the side effects of that glass of wine on the immune system counteracts the possible benefits of the wine on the heart. There are two other factors which counteract this argument. Firstly, this daily drip drip of alcohol into the body means the liver is constantly at work neutralising it, which is fine in the first half of your life, but after a time does increase metabolic ageing. And secondly, unless you are drinking only the finest quality organic wines, the very high levels of chemicals and pesticides used by many vineyards will eventually build up in your system.

NOTES AND OBSERVATIONS

# DAY 84

**TODAYS DATE** ..................................................................................................................................

**Quality of sleep:** ...............................**Number of hours slept**: ....................................................

Scale: 1 = poor  Scale: 10 = deep and refreshing

**Vitality factor in morning** (scale 1= very tired, hungover, not well, dying)

(scale: 10 = full of energy, clear headed, refreshed, generally fantastic) ............................................out of 10

**Breakfast**

Time eaten: ...........................................

Food:..................................................................................................................................

..................................................................................................................................

**Snack**

Time eaten: ...........................................

Food:..................................................................................................................................

..................................................................................................................................

**Lunch**

Time eaten: ...........................................

Food:..................................................................................................................................

..................................................................................................................................

..................................................................................................................................

**Snack**

Time eaten: ...........................................

Food:..................................................................................................................................

..................................................................................................................................

**Dinner**

Time eaten: ...........................................

Food:..................................................................................................................................

..................................................................................................................................

..................................................................................................................................

**Exercise**: ............................................................................................................................

..................................................................................................................................

**Quality of day out of 10**.......................................................................................................

The best wines to drink are of course quality-matured wines from organic vineyards, where the majority of the yeast has been used up in the fermentation of the sugars into alcohol. If you suspect you are yeast intolerant, it is least damaging to drink fine dry white wine and Champagnes. Red wines tend to contain more yeast. If you are intolerant to alcohol or yeast, you will get drunk very quickly and/or feel very sleepy after drinking a small quantity of wine. Hangovers are often not commensurate with the small amount you have drunk.

## Washing up liquid

Wear gloves and always rinse your dishes and cutlery well!! This stuff is poisonous and has been brought up time and time again as a possible cancer cause when I have asked the body. Or alternatively, use products which are chemical free, natural and break down in the water table in three days, compared to 26 years for all chemically based detergents. These are available in most good health shops.

## Wheat

My experience with wheat personally and in the multitude of health problems it causes in hundreds of my clients prompts me to state that I believe modern day wheat to be responsible for many health problems today. These include diabetes, irritable bowel problems, constipation, migraines and headaches, back problems, heart attacks, strokes, allergies, ADDH and hormonal imbalances to name a few common ones. Wheat feeds viruses and damages the immune system in around 90% of my clients.

In the late 1860's, man began to selectively breed wheat to increase the yield of the crop. They took the original wheat grain we now call Spelt, and through cross-pollination increased the size of the germ twofold and in doing so doubled the gluten content. The gluten is the part of the wheat that causes the springiness and chewiness of modern day breads. However, before long, the new grains became more and more susceptible to attack by bugs and fungus and it became necessary to increase the toughness of the husk surrounding the germ to protect it. That husk is now as tough as PVC and even hydrochloric acid struggles to dissolve it. Our digestive systems also struggle and very few people seem to be able to digest it easily without any impact on either the digestive tract or immune

# DAY 85

**TODAYS DATE** ...................................................................................................................................................................

**Quality of sleep:** ...............................**Number of hours slept**: .........................................................................................
Scale: 1 = poor   Scale: 10 = deep and refreshing

**Vitality factor in morning**  (scale 1= very tired, hungover, not well, dying)
(scale: 10 = full of energy, clear headed, refreshed, generally fantastic) ........................................................out of 10

**Breakfast**

Time eaten: .........................................

Food:...............................................................................................................................................................
........................................................................................................................................................................

**Snack**

Time eaten: .........................................

Food:...............................................................................................................................................................
........................................................................................................................................................................

**Lunch**

Time eaten: .........................................

Food:...............................................................................................................................................................
........................................................................................................................................................................
........................................................................................................................................................................

**Snack**

Time eaten: .........................................

Food:...............................................................................................................................................................
........................................................................................................................................................................

**Dinner**

Time eaten: .........................................

Food:...............................................................................................................................................................
........................................................................................................................................................................
........................................................................................................................................................................

**Exercise**: ..........................................................................................................................................................
........................................................................................................................................................................

**Quality of day out of 10** .................................................................................................................................

system. Modern day wheat is a completely different grain than the ancient wheat grain of our ancestors. It is also our staple diet and we eat far more than our bodies can digest and detoxify from. Spelt flour is still grown in a few specialised farms around the world and is becoming more and more readily available for home baking.

Problems that have disappeared when wheat has been eliminated from the diets of my clients (for a minimum of two months) have included bloating, reflux, gas, headaches, urticaria, acne, joint pain, arthritis, sinus pain, rhinitis, dandruff, fatigue, itchiness, muscle injuries, back pain, haemorrhoids, inflammation in the joints and tightness in the chest. Of the eight people I have talked to who had survived a heart attack, the body reported wheat as 80% of the direct cause in five of them. When they eliminated wheat, further tests done three months later showed that the arteries were less furred up. In one patient who was 70 years old, the furring up of his heart arteries opened up from 80% down to 20% over a year as confirmed by medical tests. The impact of modern day wheat on health needs to be seriously researched.

## Warts

According to the body, a virus, the Human Papillary Virus, is kept alive when it feeds on certain foods that you are eating, causing warts. When you avoid these foods strictly for 2 to 3 months, the virus starves and dies and the warts drop off. These foods are wheat, fructose found in all fruit except lemon, lime and grapefruit, sucrose and honey. It is difficult but necessary to avoid these foods for 6 weeks to starve the virus. The herb Barberry, taken in conjunction with the diet, will kill this virus on its own but is helped if these foods are drastically reduced. Take Barberry in capsule form 1500mg daily, or in liquid form 10 drops x 2 daily for 3 months. This information was prescribed by my client's bodies and has been tested and proven every time we have tried it to date. If it works for you, please e-mail me so I can add you to the study: www.judycole.co.uk

**WEIGH AND MEASURE DAY**

weight...................... kgs/lbs
waist ............................. cm
hips .............................. cm
bust/chest ...................... cm
top of thigh ..................... cm
top of arm ...................... cm
knee ............................. cm
calf............................... cm

**Weekly marks out of 10**
Sleep quality ........................
Average no hours slept...........
AM vitality factor..................
Quality of week ....................
Adherence to programme.......
No of days exercised ............

NOTES AND OBSERVATIONS
..............................................
..............................................
..............................................
..............................................
..............................................
..............................................

# DAY 86

**TODAYS DATE** ...............................................................................................................................................................

**Quality of sleep:** ................................**Number of hours slept**: .............................................................................

Scale: 1 = poor  Scale: 10 = deep and refreshing

**Vitality factor in morning** (scale 1= very tired, hungover, not well, dying)

(scale: 10 = full of energy, clear headed, refreshed, generally fantastic) .............................................................out of 10

**Breakfast**

Time eaten: ......................................

Food:.........................................................................................................................................................

................................................................................................................................................................

**Snack**

Time eaten: ......................................

Food:.........................................................................................................................................................

................................................................................................................................................................

**Lunch**

Time eaten: ......................................

Food:.........................................................................................................................................................

................................................................................................................................................................

................................................................................................................................................................

**Snack**

Time eaten: ......................................

Food:.........................................................................................................................................................

................................................................................................................................................................

**Dinner**

Time eaten: ......................................

Food:.........................................................................................................................................................

................................................................................................................................................................

................................................................................................................................................................

**Exercise**: ....................................................................................................................................................

................................................................................................................................................................

**Quality of day out of 10**.............................................................................................................................

## X is for...

### Xcess

Excess of anything will always make you fat and throw you out of balance. Everything in nature is balanced and to be aligned with our bodies and nature, moderation and balance are a great mantra. Just as it is important to feed our bodies a combination and variety of natural foods, so it is good to feed the soul occasionally with the things we love and the odd treat or good party. Sadly by the time we surfeit on the foods that are not good for us, so sickening the appetite for them, it is not only the appetite that dies but our life source!

## Y is for...

### Yoghurt

Yoghurt is made when live cultures of bacteria are added to milk to curdle it. The harmless bacteria, commonly known as acidophilus and bifidus, break down the sugars known as lactose in milk and turn them into lactic acid which then curdles the fresh milk to make yoghurt. Because the lactose is broken down, live yoghurt can be eaten by anyone intolerant to the lactose in milk and eaten without any problem. To ensure complete digestion, the yoghurt should still contain live bacteria, which should be labelled on the carton. Most yoghurts which have had sugar and fruit added to them or are long-life, will no longer be live and are less beneficial to the gut. These good bacteria are vital for good colon health and for the complete breakdown of foods. A vital vitamin, vitamin K, is manufactured for the body by acidophilus and bifidus and it is a good idea to regularly eat live yoghurt or take an acidophilus supplement from time to time to ensure that there is sufficient good bacteria in your digestive tract. The bodies of several women suffering with fibroids told me that the cause of these incurable growths was a lack of vitamin K. When they took acidophilus for a year, their fibroids shrank and disappeared, without the need for any surgery or medical intervention. Every case of fibroids I have treated has responded to this intervention. A lack of vitamin K also appears to increase the production of scar tissue and adhesions in the body, and acidophilus and extra live plain yoghurt should be taken before and after any operation, for several months to reduce both these side effects of damage to tissue.

NOTES AND OBSERVATIONS

..................................
..................................
..................................
..................................
..................................
..................................
..................................
..................................
..................................
..................................
..................................
..................................
..................................
..................................
..................................
..................................
..................................
..................................
..................................
..................................
..................................
..................................
..................................
..................................
..................................
..................................
..................................
..................................

# DAY 87

**TODAYS DATE** ...........................................................................................................................................................................

**Quality of sleep:** .................................**Number of hours slept**: ..............................................................................
Scale: 1 = poor  Scale: 10 = deep and refreshing

**Vitality factor in morning**  (scale 1= very tired, hungover, not well, dying)
(scale: 10 = full of energy, clear headed, refreshed, generally fantastic) ...........................................................out of 10

**Breakfast**

Time eaten: ...........................................
Food:.......................................................................................................................................................................
...............................................................................................................................................................................

**Snack**

Time eaten: ...........................................
Food:.......................................................................................................................................................................
...............................................................................................................................................................................

**Lunch**

Time eaten: ...........................................
Food:.......................................................................................................................................................................
...............................................................................................................................................................................
...............................................................................................................................................................................

**Snack**

Time eaten: ...........................................
Food:.......................................................................................................................................................................
...............................................................................................................................................................................

**Dinner**

Time eaten: ...........................................
Food:.......................................................................................................................................................................
...............................................................................................................................................................................
...............................................................................................................................................................................

**Exercise**: .............................................................................................................................................................
...............................................................................................................................................................................
**Quality of day out of 10**.......................................................................................................................................

161

## Z is for...

### Zzzzzzz's

Optimum sleep is a luxury in our busy lives but just as getting enough is vital, getting too much can also be detrimental. However, when you are toxic, your body will automatically need more in order to spend more time trying to detoxify the build up during the day. As you go through this programme, you will find you have days of needing far more sleep as the body tries to knock you out in order to heal more deeply. As you heal you will find that you need less and less sleep as time goes by. Rather than go to bed late and wake up by an alarm, go to bed earlier during the programme and allow your body to wake you when you have had enough rest. You may be surprised at how soon you begin to wake early before the alarm. It is common to have days of feeling almost drugged with tiredness in the first few weeks of detox. A toxic system will need eight to nine hours of sleep to recover. A clean body should only need six and a half to seven, depending of course on your activity level during the day.

NOTES AND OBSERVATIONS

..................................
..................................
..................................
..................................
..................................
..................................
..................................
..................................
..................................
..................................
..................................
..................................
..................................
..................................
..................................
..................................
..................................
..................................
..................................
..................................
..................................
..................................
..................................
..................................
..................................
..................................
..................................
..................................
..................................
..................................
..................................
..................................

# DAY 88

**TODAYS DATE**...........................................................................................................................

**Quality of sleep:** ...................................**Number of hours slept**:...........................................

Scale: 1 = poor  Scale: 10 = deep and refreshing

**Vitality factor in morning** (scale 1= very tired, hungover, not well, dying)

(scale: 10 = full of energy, clear headed, refreshed, generally fantastic) ..............................................out of 10

**Breakfast**

Time eaten: ......................................

Food:...........................................................................................................................................

...................................................................................................................................................

**Snack**

Time eaten: ......................................

Food:...........................................................................................................................................

...................................................................................................................................................

**Lunch**

Time eaten: ......................................

Food:...........................................................................................................................................

...................................................................................................................................................

...................................................................................................................................................

**Snack**

Time eaten: ......................................

Food:...........................................................................................................................................

...................................................................................................................................................

**Dinner**

Time eaten: ......................................

Food:...........................................................................................................................................

...................................................................................................................................................

...................................................................................................................................................

**Exercise**:....................................................................................................................................

...................................................................................................................................................

**Quality of day out of 10**.............................................................................................................

**Weight Loss Graph**

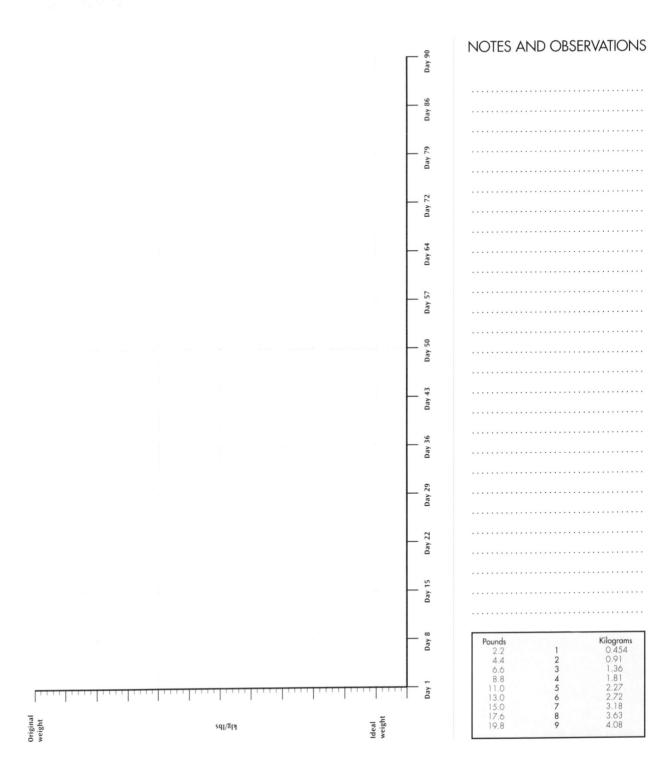

Original weight

klg/lbs

Ideal weight

Day 1
Day 8
Day 15
Day 22
Day 29
Day 36
Day 43
Day 50
Day 57
Day 64
Day 72
Day 79
Day 86
Day 90

## NOTES AND OBSERVATIONS

. . . . . . . . . . . . . . . . . . . . . . . . . . . . . . . . . .
. . . . . . . . . . . . . . . . . . . . . . . . . . . . . . . . . .
. . . . . . . . . . . . . . . . . . . . . . . . . . . . . . . . . .
. . . . . . . . . . . . . . . . . . . . . . . . . . . . . . . . . .
. . . . . . . . . . . . . . . . . . . . . . . . . . . . . . . . . .
. . . . . . . . . . . . . . . . . . . . . . . . . . . . . . . . . .
. . . . . . . . . . . . . . . . . . . . . . . . . . . . . . . . . .
. . . . . . . . . . . . . . . . . . . . . . . . . . . . . . . . . .
. . . . . . . . . . . . . . . . . . . . . . . . . . . . . . . . . .
. . . . . . . . . . . . . . . . . . . . . . . . . . . . . . . . . .
. . . . . . . . . . . . . . . . . . . . . . . . . . . . . . . . . .
. . . . . . . . . . . . . . . . . . . . . . . . . . . . . . . . . .
. . . . . . . . . . . . . . . . . . . . . . . . . . . . . . . . . .
. . . . . . . . . . . . . . . . . . . . . . . . . . . . . . . . . .
. . . . . . . . . . . . . . . . . . . . . . . . . . . . . . . . . .
. . . . . . . . . . . . . . . . . . . . . . . . . . . . . . . . . .
. . . . . . . . . . . . . . . . . . . . . . . . . . . . . . . . . .
. . . . . . . . . . . . . . . . . . . . . . . . . . . . . . . . . .
. . . . . . . . . . . . . . . . . . . . . . . . . . . . . . . . . .
. . . . . . . . . . . . . . . . . . . . . . . . . . . . . . . . . .
. . . . . . . . . . . . . . . . . . . . . . . . . . . . . . . . . .
. . . . . . . . . . . . . . . . . . . . . . . . . . . . . . . . . .
. . . . . . . . . . . . . . . . . . . . . . . . . . . . . . . . . .
. . . . . . . . . . . . . . . . . . . . . . . . . . . . . . . . . .
. . . . . . . . . . . . . . . . . . . . . . . . . . . . . . . . . .
. . . . . . . . . . . . . . . . . . . . . . . . . . . . . . . . . .

| Pounds | | Kilograms |
|---|---|---|
| 2.2 | 1 | 0.454 |
| 4.4 | 2 | 0.91 |
| 6.6 | 3 | 1.36 |
| 8.8 | 4 | 1.81 |
| 11.0 | 5 | 2.27 |
| 13.0 | 6 | 2.72 |
| 15.0 | 7 | 3.18 |
| 17.6 | 8 | 3.63 |
| 19.8 | 9 | 4.08 |

# DAY 89

**TODAYS DATE** ................................................................................................................................................................

**Quality of sleep:** .......................................**Number of hours slept**: ...............................................................................
Scale: 1 = poor  Scale: 10 = deep and refreshing

**Vitality factor in morning** (scale 1= very tired, hungover, not well, dying)
(scale: 10 = full of energy, clear headed, refreshed, generally fantastic) ....................................................................out of 10

**Breakfast**

Time eaten: ..............................................

Food:................................................................................................................................................................

................................................................................................................................................................

**Snack**

Time eaten: ..............................................

Food:................................................................................................................................................................

................................................................................................................................................................

**Lunch**

Time eaten: ..............................................

Food:................................................................................................................................................................

................................................................................................................................................................

................................................................................................................................................................

**Snack**

Time eaten: ..............................................

Food:................................................................................................................................................................

................................................................................................................................................................

**Dinner**

Time eaten: ..............................................

Food:................................................................................................................................................................

................................................................................................................................................................

................................................................................................................................................................

**Exercise**: ........................................................................................................................................................

................................................................................................................................................................

**Quality of day out of 10**.........................................................................................................................................

## Quality of Life Graph

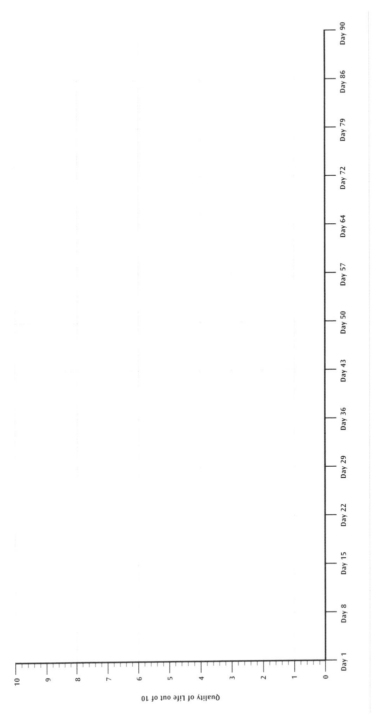

Quality of Life out of 10

Day 1 · Day 8 · Day 15 · Day 22 · Day 29 · Day 36 · Day 43 · Day 50 · Day 57 · Day 64 · Day 72 · Day 79 · Day 86 · Day 90

10 · 9 · 8 · 7 · 6 · 5 · 4 · 3 · 2 · 1 · 0

**WEIGH AND MEASURE DAY**

weight...................... kgs/lbs
waist ............................. cm
hips ................................ cm
bust/chest ...................... cm
top of thigh..................... cm
top of arm ...................... cm
knee ............................... cm
calf................................ cm

Weekly marks out of 10
Sleep quality ........................
Average no hours slept...........
AM vitality factor...................
Quality of week ....................
Adherence to programme.......
No of days exercised ............

NOTES AND OBSERVATIONS

.................................................
.................................................
.................................................
.................................................
.................................................
.................................................

# DAY 90

**TODAYS DATE**......................................................................................................................................................

**Quality of sleep:** ................................**Number of hours slept**:...........................................................................
Scale: 1 = poor  Scale: 10 = deep and refreshing

**Vitality factor in morning**  (scale 1= very tired, hungover, not well, dying)
(scale: 10 = full of energy, clear headed, refreshed, generally fantastic) ..................................................out of 10

**Breakfast**

Time eaten: ...........................................

Food:.......................................................................................................................................................

.......................................................................................................................................................

**Snack**

Time eaten: ...........................................

Food:.......................................................................................................................................................

.......................................................................................................................................................

**Lunch**

Time eaten: ...........................................

Food:.......................................................................................................................................................

.......................................................................................................................................................

.......................................................................................................................................................

**Snack**

Time eaten: ...........................................

Food:.......................................................................................................................................................

.......................................................................................................................................................

**Dinner**

Time eaten: ...........................................

Food:.......................................................................................................................................................

.......................................................................................................................................................

.......................................................................................................................................................

**Exercise**:..............................................................................................................................................

.......................................................................................................................................................

**Quality of day out of 10**.............................................................................................................................

## Index A–Z

## NOTES AND OBSERVATIONS

...........................
...........................
...........................
...........................
...........................
...........................
...........................
...........................
...........................
...........................
...........................
...........................
...........................
...........................
...........................
...........................
...........................
...........................
...........................
...........................
...........................
...........................
...........................
...........................
...........................
...........................
...........................
...........................
...........................
...........................
...........................
...........................
...........................
...........................
...........................
...........................
...........................
...........................
...........................
...........................